FANTASTIC BEASTS

AND WHERE TO FIND THEM™

THE ORIGINAL SCREENPLAY

J.K. ROWLING

FANTASTIC BEASTS

AND WHERE TO FIND THEM™

THE ORIGINAL SCREENPLAY

COVER AND BOOK DESIGN
BY
MINALIMA

Little, Brown

LITTLE, BROWN

First published in print in Great Britain in 2016 by Little, Brown

3 5 7 9 10 8 6 4 2

A CIP catalogue record for this book
is available from the British Library.

ISBN 978-1-4087-0898-9

Typeset in Crimson by MinaLima
Printed and bound in Great Britain by Clays Ltd, St Ives plc

Papers used by Little, Brown are from well-managed forests
and other responsible sources.

MIX
Paper from
responsible sources
FSC
www.fsc.org   FSC® C104740

Little, Brown
An imprint of
Little, Brown Book Group
Carmelite House
50 Victoria Embankment
London EC4Y 0DZ

An Hachette UK Company
www.hachette.co.uk

www.littlebrown.co.uk

To the memory of Gordon Murray,
real-life creature-healer and hero

CONTENTS

Fantastic Beasts and Where to Find Them:
The Original Screenplay

1

Acknowledgements
285

Glossary of Film Terms
287

Cast and Crew
289

About the Author
291

About the Book Design
293

SCENE 1
EXT. SOMEWHERE IN EUROPE—1926—NIGHT

A large, isolated, derelict chateau emerges from the darkness. We focus on a cobbled square outside the building shrouded in mist, eerie, silent.

Five Aurors stand, wands aloft, tentative as they edge towards the chateau. A sudden explosion of pure white light sends them flying.

*We whip round to find their bodies scattered, lying motionless at the entrance to a large parkland. A figure (*GRINDELWALD*) enters the frame, his back to the camera; ignoring the bodies, he stares out into the night sky, as we pan up towards the moon.*

MONTAGE: we see various magical newspaper headlines from 1926 relating to GRINDELWALD'S *attacks all*

*over the world – 'GRINDELWALD STRIKES AGAIN
IN EUROPE', 'HOGWARTS SCHOOL INCREASES
SECURITY', 'WHERE IS GRINDELWALD?'. He's a
serious threat to the magical community and he's vanished.
Moving photos detail destroyed buildings, fires, screaming
victims. The articles come thick and fast – the worldwide
hunt for* GRINDELWALD *continues. We push in on a final
article displaying the Statue of Liberty.*

TRANSITION TO:

SCENE 2
EXT. SHIP GLIDING INTO NEW YORK—NEXT MORNING

A bright, clear New York day. Seagulls swoop overhead.

*A large passenger ship glides past the Statue of Liberty. Passengers
lean over the rails, looking excitedly towards the oncoming land.*

*PUSH IN towards a figure sitting on a bench with his
back to us –* NEWT SCAMANDER, *weatherbeaten, wiry,
wearing an old blue overcoat. Beside him rests a battered
brown leather case. A catch on the case flicks open of its
own accord.* NEWT *swiftly bends down to close it.*

Placing the case on his lap, NEWT *leans in, whispering.*

> NEWT
> Dougal – you settle down
> now, please. It won't be long.

SCENE 3
EXT. NEW YORK—DAY

AERIAL SHOT of New York.

SCENE 4
EXT. SHIP/INT. CUSTOMS—SHORTLY
AFTERWARDS—DAY

Among bustling crowds, NEWT *walks down the gangplank of the ship, as we push in towards his case.*

> CUSTOMS OFFICIAL (*O.S.*)
> Next.

NEWT *stands at the Customs – a long row of desks by the shipyard, manned by serious-looking American officials. A* CUSTOMS OFFICIAL *examines* NEWT'S *very tattered British passport.*

> CUSTOMS OFFICIAL
> British, huh?

> NEWT
> Yes.

> CUSTOMS OFFICIAL
> First trip to New York?

> NEWT
> Yes.

> CUSTOMS OFFICIAL
> (*gesturing to* NEWT'S *case*)
> Anything edible in there?

> NEWT
> (*placing a hand over his breast pocket*)
> No.

> CUSTOMS OFFICIAL
> Livestock?

The catch on NEWT'S *case flicks open again.* NEWT *looks down and hastily closes it.*

NEWT
Must get that fixed – ah, no.

CUSTOMS OFFICIAL
(*suspicious*)
Let me take a look.

NEWT *places the case on the desk between them and discreetly flicks a brass dial to 'Muggleworthy'.*

The CUSTOMS OFFICIAL *spins the case towards him and pops the catches, lifting the lid to reveal pyjamas, various maps, a journal, an alarm clock, a magnifying glass and a Hufflepuff scarf. Finally satisfied, he closes the case.*

CUSTOMS OFFICIAL
Welcome to New York.

NEWT
Thank you.

NEWT *gathers his passport and case.*

CUSTOMS OFFICIAL
Next!

NEWT *exits through Customs.*

SCENE 5
EXT. STREET NEAR CITY HALL SUBWAY— DUSK

A long street of identical brownstone houses, one of which has been reduced to rubble. A gaggle of reporters and photographers mills around in the vague hope of something happening, but without much enthusiasm. One REPORTER *is interviewing an excitable middle-aged man as they move through the rubble.*

> WITNESS
> —and it was like a – like a
> *wind* or like a – like a *ghost* –
> but dark – and I saw its
> eyes – shinin' white eyes—

> REPORTER
> *(expressionless – notebook*
> *in his hand)*
> —a dark wind – with eyes …

> WITNESS
> —like a dark *mass*, and it
> dove down there, down
> underground – I swear to
> God … into the earth right in
> front of me.

CLOSE ON PERCIVAL GRAVES *as he walks towards the destroyed building.*

GRAVES: *smart clothing, very handsome, early middle-age, his demeanour differs from those around him. He is watchful, tightly coiled, an air of intense confidence.*

> PHOTOGRAPHER
> *(sotto voce)*
> Hey – did you get anything?

> REPORTER
> *(sotto voce)*
> Dark wind, blah blah.

> PHOTOGRAPHER
> It's some atmospheric hooey.
> Or electrical.

GRAVES *moves up the steps of the now-ruined building.*
He examines the destruction, curious, alert.

REPORTER
Hey – you thirsty?

PHOTOGRAPHER
Nah, I'm on the wagon.
Promised Martha I'd lay off.

The wind begins to pick up, swirling around the building,
accompanied by a high-pitched screeching. GRAVES *alone*
looks interested.

A sudden series of bangs at street level. All turn to look for
the source of the sound: a wall cracks, the rubble on the floor
begins to shake before exploding like an earthquake, ripping
out of the building and down through the middle of the street.
The movement is violent, rushed – people and cars go flying.

The mysterious force then flies up into the air, swirling
through the city, diving in and out of alleyways, before
crashing down into a subway station.

CLOSE ON GRAVES, *as he examines the destruction of*
the street.

A mingled roar and howl emanates from the bowels of the
earth.

SCENE 6
EXT. NEW YORK STREET—DAY

Watching NEWT *walk, we see in him an unselfconscious Keatonesque quality, a sense of a different rhythm to those around him. In his hand he clutches directions on a small piece of paper, but he still shows a scientist's curiosity about this alien environment.*

SCENE 7
EXT. ANOTHER STREET, STEPS OF THE CITY BANK—DAY

NEWT, *intrigued by the noise of shouting, approaches a rally of the New Salem Philanthropic Society.*

MARY LOU BAREBONE, *a handsome mid-western woman in a 1920s version of Puritan dress, charismatic and earnest, stands on a small stage at the steps to the City Bank. Behind her stands a man parading a banner emblazoned with the organisation's symbol: hands*

*proudly grasping a broken wand amid bright yellow and
red flames.*

> MARY LOU
> *(to the assembled crowd)*
> ... this great city sparkles
> with the jewels of man's
> invention! Movie theatres,
> automobiles, the wireless,
> electric lights – all dazzle and
> bewitch us!

NEWT *slows down and watches* MARY LOU *as he would
observe a foreign species: no judgement, simply interest.
Nearby stands* TINA GOLDSTEIN, *hat low on her head,
upturned collar. She is eating a hot dog, mustard smeared
on her upper lip.* NEWT *accidently bumps into her as he
makes his way to the front of the rally.*

> NEWT
> Oh ... so sorry.

> MARY LOU
> But where there is light there
> is shadow, friend.
> Something is stalking our
> city, wreaking destruction
> and then disappearing
> without a trace ...

JACOB KOWALSKI *moves nervously down the street towards the crowd, wearing an ill-fitting suit and carrying a battered brown leather case.*

> MARY LOU (*O.S.*)
> We have to fight – join us, the
> Second Salemers, in our fight!

JACOB *makes his way through the gathered crowd, also pushing past* TINA.

> JACOB
> Excuse me doll, just trying to
> get to the bank – excuse me –
> just trying ...

JACOB *trips over* NEWT'S *case, disappearing momentarily.* NEWT *hauls him up.*

> NEWT
> I'm so sorry – my case—

> JACOB
> No harm done—

JACOB *struggles on, heading past* MARY LOU *and up the steps of the bank.*

> JACOB
> Excuse me!

The kerfuffle around NEWT *draws* MARY LOU'S
attention.

> MARY LOU
> (*charming, to* NEWT)
> You, friend! What drew you
> to our meeting today?

NEWT *is startled to find himself the centre of attention.*

> NEWT
> Oh ... I was just ... passing ...

> MARY LOU
> Are you a seeker? A seeker
> after truth?

A beat.

> NEWT
> I'm more of a chaser, really.

ANGLE ON people moving in and out of the bank.

A *smartly dressed man flips a dime towards a beggar sitting
on the steps.*

CLOSE ON the dime, falling in slow motion.

> MARY LOU (*O.S.*)
> Hear my words and heed my
> warning ...

ANGLE ON some little paws, which have appeared in the narrow crack between the lid and the body of NEWT'S *case.*

ANGLE ON the dime hitting the steps with a musical clang.

ANGLE ON the paws, now trying hard to prise open the case.

> MARY LOU
> ... and laugh if you dare:
> *witches live among us!*

MARY LOU'S *three adopted children, adults* CREDENCE *and* CHASTITY, *and* MODESTY (*an eight-year-old girl), hand out leaflets.* CREDENCE *appears nervous and troubled.*

> MARY LOU (*O.S.*)
> We have to fight together for
> the sake of our children – for
> the sake of tomorrow!
> (*to* NEWT)
> What do you say to that,
> friend?

As NEWT *looks up towards* MARY LOU, *something seen from the corner of his eye catches his attention. The Niffler, a small furry black cross between a mole and a duck-billed platypus, is sitting on the steps of the bank, hastily pulling the beggar's hat full of money out of sight behind a pillar.*

NEWT, *startled, looks down at his case.*

ANGLE ON the Niffler, busy shovelling the beggar's coins into a pouch in its belly. The Niffler looks up, notices NEWT'S *gaze, and hurriedly gathers the rest of the coins before tumbling away and into the bank.*

NEWT *jolts forwards.*

>   NEWT
>   Excuse me.

ANGLE ON MARY LOU – *she looks confused at* NEWT'S *lack of interest in her cause.*

>   MARY LOU (*O.S.*)
>   Witches live among us.

ANGLE ON TINA, *moving through the crowd, eyeing* NEWT *suspiciously.*

SCENE 8
INT. LOBBY OF BANK—MOMENTS LATER—DAY

A large, impressive-looking bank atrium. In the centre, behind a golden counter, clerks are busy at work serving customers.

NEWT *skids to a halt in the entrance of the space and looks around for his creature. His dress and demeanour make him out of place among the smartly dressed New Yorkers.*

> BANK EMPLOYEE
> *(suspicious)*
> Can I help you, sir?

> NEWT
> No, I was just … just …
> waiting …

NEWT *motions towards a bench and backs away, taking a seat next to* JACOB.

TINA *peers at* NEWT *from behind a pillar.*

> JACOB
> *(nervous)*
> Hi. What brings you here?

NEWT *is desperately trying to spot his Niffler.*

> NEWT
> Same as you ...

> JACOB
> You're here to get a loan to
> open up a bakery?

> NEWT
> *(looking around –*
> *preoccupied)*
> Yes.

> JACOB
> What are the odds of that?
> Well, may the best man win,
> I guess.

NEWT *spots the Niffler, which is now stealing coins from someone's bag.*

JACOB *holds out his hand, but* NEWT *is off.*

> NEWT
> Excuse me.

NEWT *darts away. In his place on the bench lies a large silver egg.*

> JACOB
> Hey, mister ... hey mister!

NEWT *doesn't hear; he is too engaged in hunting the Niffler.*

JACOB *picks up the egg just as the door into the* BANK MANAGER'S *office opens, and a* SECRETARY *looks out.*

> JACOB
> Hey, fella!

> SECRETARY
> Mr Kowalski, Mr Bingley will
> see you now.

Pocketing the egg, JACOB *heads towards the office, steeling himself.*

> JACOB
> *(sotto voce)*
> Okay ... okay.

ANGLE ON NEWT, *surreptitiously pursuing the Niffler as it moves through the bank. He finally spots it removing a glittering buckle from a lady's shoe before scurrying onwards, eager for more shiny objects.*

As NEWT *watches, helpless, the Niffler jumps lithely between cases and into bags, snatching and pilfering.*

SCENE 9
INT. BINGLEY'S OFFICE—MOMENTS LATER—DAY

JACOB *is facing the imposing and impeccably suited* MR BINGLEY. BINGLEY *is examining* JACOB'S *business proposal for a bakery.*

An uncomfortable silence. The sound of a ticking clock and BINGLEY *murmuring.*

JACOB *looks down at his pocket – the egg has started to vibrate.*

> BINGLEY
> You are currently working ...
> in a canning factory?

> JACOB
> That's the best I can do – I
> only got back in '24.

> BINGLEY

Got back?

> JACOB

From Europe, sir. Yeah – I
was part of the Expeditionary
Forces there—

JACOB *is clearly nervous, miming a digging action to the
words 'Expeditionary Forces', in the vain hope that a joke
might help his cause.*

SCENE 10
INT. BACK ROOM OF THE BANK—MOMENTS
LATER—DAY

We cut back to NEWT *in the bank – in seeking the Niffler
he has ended up waiting in line for a bank teller. He cranes
his neck, peering towards the bag of a lady at the front of
the line.* TINA *watches him from behind a pillar.*

ANGLE ON coins spilling from underneath a bench.

ANGLE ON NEWT, *who hears the coins and turns to see
small paws hastily gathering them up.*

ANGLE ON the Niffler sitting under the bench looking fat and smug. Not yet satisfied, its attention is caught by the shiny tag hanging around the neck of a small dog. The Niffler moves slowly, cheekily, forwards – little paw outstretched to grab the tag. The dog snarls and barks.

NEWT *starts forwards and dives under the bench – the Niffler runs, scuttling over the bank counter screens and out of* NEWT'S *reach.*

SCENE 11
INT. BINGLEY'S OFFICE—MOMENTS LATER—DAY

JACOB *opens his case with great pride. Inside is displayed a selection of his home-made pastries.*

> JACOB (*O.S.*)
> All right.

> BINGLEY
> Mr Kowalski—

> JACOB
> —you gotta try the paczki
> okay, it's my grandmother's
> recipe, the orange zest – just—

JACOB *holds out a paczki ... * BINGLEY *is not distracted.*

> BINGLEY
> Mr Kowalski, what do you
> propose to offer the bank as
> collateral?

> JACOB
> Collateral?

> BINGLEY
> Collateral.

JACOB *gestures hopefully towards his pastries.*

> BINGLEY
> There are machines now that
> can produce hundreds of
> doughnuts an hour—

> JACOB
> I know, I know, but they're
> nothing like what I can do—

BINGLEY
The bank must be protected,
Mr Kowalski. Good day to
you.

BINGLEY *dismissively rings a bell on his desk.*

SCENE 12
INT. BEHIND THE BANK COUNTERS—
MOMENTS LATER—DAY

The Niffler sits on a trolley covered in money bags, which it greedily empties into its pouch. As NEWT *watches through the security bars, aghast, a guard pushes the trolley away down a corridor.*

SCENE 13
INT. BANK, HALL—MOMENTS LATER—DAY

JACOB, *downcast, exits* BINGLEY'S *office. His bulging*

*pocket vibrates. Alarmed, he pulls out the egg and looks
around.*

*ANGLE ON the Niffler, still sitting on the trolley, which is
now being pushed into an elevator.*

ANGLE ON JACOB, *who sees* NEWT *in the distance.*

> JACOB
> Hey, Mr English guy! I think
> your egg is hatching.

NEWT *looks hurriedly between* JACOB *and the shutting
elevator doors before making a decision: he points his wand
at* JACOB. JACOB *and the egg are pulled magically across
the bank atrium towards* NEWT. *In a split second, they
Disapparate.*

TINA *stares, incredulous, from behind a pillar.*

SCENE 14
INT. BACK ROOM OF THE BANK/STAIRCASE—
DAY

NEWT *and* JACOB *Apparate into a narrow stairwell*

leading to the bank's vaults, suddenly past the tellers and
security guards.

NEWT *gently takes the egg back from* JACOB *as it hatches,*
revealing a small blue, snake-like bird – an Occamy.
NEWT, *his face full of wonder, looks to* JACOB *as though*
expecting a similar reaction from him.

Slowly, NEWT *carries the baby creature down the stairs.*

JACOB

Excuse me ...

JACOB, *very confused, looks back up the stairs towards the*
main bank atrium. On seeing BINGLEY *approaching, he*
ducks down the stairs, out of sight.

JACOB
(to himself)

I was – over there. I was –
over there?

SCENE 15
INT. BASEMENT CORRIDOR OF BANK
LEADING TO VAULT—DAY

JACOB'S *POV:* NEWT *is crouched down, opening his case.*
He carefully places the hatched Occamy inside, whispering
tenderly:

> NEWT
>
> In you hop ...

> JACOB (*O.S.*)
>
> Hello?

> NEWT
>
> No. Everyone settle down –
> stay. Dougal, don't make me
> come in there ...

JACOB *moves along the corridor, staring at* NEWT.

We see a strange green creature, part stick insect, part
plant, poke its head out of NEWT'S *breast pocket,*
intrigued. This is PICKETT, *a Bowtruckle.*

> NEWT
>
> Don't make me come down
> there.

NEWT *looks up to see the Niffler squeezing itself through locked doors, into the central vault.*

> NEWT
> Absolutely not!

NEWT *takes out his wand and points it at the vault.*

> NEWT
> *Alohomora.*

We watch the locks and cogs of the vault door turn.

BINGLEY *comes round the corner, just as the vault door starts to open.*

> BINGLEY
> (*to* JACOB)
> Oh, so you're gonna STEAL
> the money, huh?

BINGLEY *hits a button on the wall. An alarm sounds.* NEWT *aims his wand ...*

> NEWT
> *Petrificus Totalus.*

BINGLEY *suddenly stiffens and falls back flat on the ground.* JACOB *cannot believe his eyes.*

> JACOB
> Mr Bingley!

The vault door opens wide.

> MR BINGLEY
> *(in his paralysed state)*
> ... Kowalski!

NEWT *hurries into the vault. Inside he finds the Niffler lying among hundreds of opened deposit boxes, and seated on a great pile of cash. The Niffler stares at* NEWT *defiantly as it forces another gold bar into its already overflowing pouch.*

> NEWT
> Really?!

NEWT *grasps the Niffler tightly and turns it upside down, shaking it by its hind legs. An extraordinary, and seemingly endless, number of precious items fall out.*

> NEWT
> *(to the Niffler)*
> No ...

JACOB *looks around him in disbelief, an almost queasy fear.*

Despite their altercation, NEWT *is fond of the Niffler. He grins as he tickles its stomach, causing more treasure to pour out.*

*Footsteps on the stairs as several armed guards run down
and into the vault corridor.*

> JACOB
> *(panicking)*
> Oh no ... no ... don't shoot.
> Don't shoot!

NEWT *quickly seizes* JACOB *and the two of them, plus the
Niffler and case, Disapparate.*

SCENE 16
EXT. DESERTED SIDE STREET NEXT TO THE
BANK—DAY

NEWT *and* JACOB *Apparate into a side street. Security
alarms ring out from the bank and, at the end of the side
street, we see crowds gathering, police arriving.*

TINA *runs out of the bank and looks down. She sees* NEWT
wrestling the Niffler back into the case, JACOB *cowering
by a wall.*

> JACOB
>
> Ahhh!

> NEWT
>
> For the last time, you
> pilfering pest – paws off what
> doesn't belong to you!

NEWT *shuts his case, then looks around at* JACOB.

> NEWT
>
> I'm awfully sorry about all
> that—

> JACOB
>
> What the *hell* was that?

> NEWT
>
> Nothing that need concern
> you. Now unfortunately you
> have seen far too much, so if
> you wouldn't mind – if you
> just stand there – this will be
> over in a jiffy.

NEWT, *trying to find his wand, turns his back on* JACOB.
JACOB *takes the opportunity, seizes his case, and swings it
violently at* NEWT, *who is knocked to the ground.*

> JACOB

Sorry—

JACOB *runs for his life.*

NEWT *holds his head for a moment and looks after* JACOB, *who has hurried down the alleyway and into the crowd.*

> NEWT

Bugger!

TINA *comes walking down the side street with purpose.* NEWT *gathers himself, picks up the case and, trying to be nonchalant, walks towards her. As he passes her,* TINA *grabs* NEWT'S *elbow and they Disapparate.*

SCENE 17
EXT. NARROW ALLEYWAY OPPOSITE BANK— DAY

NEWT *and* TINA *Apparate into a cramped, bricked-up alleyway. We can still hear police sirens sounding in the background.*

TINA, *incredulous and out of breath, rounds on* NEWT.

TINA
Who *are* you?

NEWT
I'm sorry?

TINA
Who *are you*?

NEWT
Newt Scamander. And you
are?

TINA
What's that *thing* in your case?

NEWT
That's my Niffler.
(*pointing at hot dog
mustard still on
TINA'S lip*)
Er, you've got something on
your—

TINA
Why in the name of
Deliverance Dane did you let
that thing loose?

NEWT

I didn't mean to – he's
incorrigible, you see, anything
shiny, he's all over the place—

TINA

You didn't mean to?

NEWT

No.

TINA

You could not have chosen
a worse time to let that
creature loose! We're in the
middle of a situation here! I'm
taking you in.

NEWT

You're taking me where?

*She produces her official ID card. It bears her moving
picture and an impressive symbol of an American eagle:
MACUSA.*

TINA

Magical Congress of the
United States of America.

NEWT
(*nervous*)
So, you work for MACUSA?
What are you, some kind of
investigator?

TINA
(*hesitates*)
Uh huh.

She stuffs her identification card back into her coat.

TINA
Can you please tell me you
took care of the No-Maj?

NEWT
The what?

TINA
(*becoming irritated*)
The No-Maj! No-magic – the
non-wizard!

NEWT
Oh sorry, we call them
Muggles.

> TINA
> (*getting really worried*)
> You wiped his memory,
> right? The No-Maj with the
> case?

> NEWT

Um ...

> TINA
> (*appalled*)
> That's a Section 3A, Mr
> Scamander. I'm taking you in.

She takes NEWT *by the arm and they Disapparate again.*

SCENE 18
EXT. BROADWAY—DAY

An ornately carved, incredibly tall skyscraper on the corner of a bustling street – the Woolworth Building.

NEWT *and* TINA *hurry along Broadway towards this building,* TINA *almost dragging* NEWT *by his coat sleeve.*

> TINA
> Come on.

> NEWT
> Er – sorry but I do have
> things to do, actually.

TINA
Well, you'll have to rearrange
them!

TINA *forcefully guides* NEWT *through the busy traffic.*

TINA
What are you doing in New
York anyway?

NEWT
I came to buy a birthday
present.

TINA
Couldn't you have done that
in London?

They have arrived outside the Woolworth Building.
Workers move in and out of a large revolving door.

NEWT
No, there's only one breeder
of Appaloosa Puffskeins in
the world and he lives in New
York, so no ...

TINA *moves* NEWT *towards a side door, guarded by a man*
in a cloaked uniform.

> TINA
> (*to the guard*)
> I got a Section 3A.

The guard immediately opens the door.

SCENE 19
**INT. WOOLWORTH BUILDING RECEPTION—
DAY**

A normal 1920s office atrium, people milling around and chatting.

> TINA (*O.S.*)
> Hey. By the way, we closed
> that guy down a year ago.
> We don't allow the breeding
> of magical creatures in New
> York.

PAN AROUND to watch TINA *come through the door with* NEWT. *As they enter, the whole entrance magically transforms from the Woolworth Building to the Magical Congress of the United States of America (MACUSA).*

SCENE 20
INT. MACUSA LOBBY—DAY

NEWT's *POV, as they move up a wide staircase and enter the main lobby – a vast, impressive space with impossibly high vaulted ceilings.*

High up, a gigantic dial with many cogs and faces emblazoned with the legend: MAGICAL EXPOSURE THREAT LEVEL. The hand on the dial points to SEVERE: UNEXPLAINED ACTIVITY. Behind hangs an imposing portrait of a majestic-looking witch: SERAPHINA PICQUERY, *MACUSA's President.*

Owls circulate, witches and wizards in 1920s dress are hard at work. TINA *guides an impressed-looking* NEWT *through the bustle. They pass several wizards sitting in a line, waiting to have their wands shined by a house-elf who operates a complex contraption of feathers.*

NEWT *and* TINA *reach an elevator. The doors open to reveal* RED, *a goblin bellboy.*

> RED
> Hey, Goldstein.

> TINA

Hey, Red.

TINA *pushes* NEWT *inside.*

SCENE 21
INT. ELEVATOR—DAY

> TINA
> (*to* RED)
> Major Investigation
> Department.

> RED
> I thought you was—

> TINA
> *Major Investigation*
> *Department!* I got a Section
> 3A!

RED *uses a long clawed stick to reach an elevator button above his head. The elevator descends.*

SCENE 22
INT. MAJOR INVESTIGATION DEPARTMENT—
DAY

CLOSE ON a newspaper – The New York Ghost –
with the headline 'MAGICAL DISTURBANCES RISK
WIZARDING EXPOSURE'.

A group of the highest-level Aurors in the organisation
are gathered together in serious discussion. Among them
are GRAVES, *examining the newspaper, his face cut and*
bruised from last night's encounter with the strange entity,
and MADAM PICQUERY *herself.*

>   MADAM PICQUERY
> The International
> Confederation is threatening
> to send a delegation. They
> think this is related to
> Grindelwald's attacks in
> Europe.

>   GRAVES
> I was there. This is a beast.
> No human could do what this

thing is capable of, Madam
President.

MADAM PICQUERY (*O.S.*)
Whatever it is, one thing's
clear – it must be stopped.
It's terrorising No-Majs, and
when No-Majs are afraid,
they attack. This could mean
exposure. It could mean war.

On hearing footsteps, the group looks round to see TINA,
who approaches cautiously, leading NEWT.

MADAM PICQUERY
(*angry but contained*)
I made your position here
quite clear, Miss Goldstein.

TINA
(*frightened*)
Yes, Madam President, but
I—

MADAM PICQUERY
You are no longer an Auror.

TINA
No, Madam President, but—

> MADAM PICQUERY
>
> Goldstein.

> TINA
>
> There's been a minor
> incident—

> MADAM PICQUERY
>
> Well, this office is currently
> concerned with very major
> incidents. Get out.

> TINA
> *(humiliated)*
>
> Yes, ma'am.

TINA *pushes a bemused-looking* NEWT *back towards the elevator.* GRAVES *looks after them, the only one to appear sympathetic.*

SCENE 23
INT. BASEMENT—DAY

The elevator descends rapidly through the long shaft.

The doors open onto a cramped, airless, windowless basement room. A painful contrast to the floor above. Clearly the place where utter no-hopers work.

TINA *leads* NEWT *past a hundred typewriters clacking away unmanned, with a tangle of glass pipes hanging down from the ceiling above them.*

As each memo or form is completed by a typewriter, it folds itself into an origami rat, which scurries up the appropriate tube to the offices above. Two rats collide and fight, tearing each other apart.

TINA *walks towards a dingy corner of the room. A sign: WAND PERMIT OFFICE.*

NEWT *ducks under it.*

SCENE 24
INT. WAND PERMIT OFFICE—DAY

The Wand Permit Office is only slightly larger than a cupboard. There are piles of unopened wand applications.

TINA *stops behind a desk, removing her coat and hat. She tries to regain her lost status in front of* NEWT *by appearing official, busying herself with papers.*

> TINA
> So, you got your wand
> permit? All foreigners have to
> have them in New York.

> NEWT
> *(lying)*
> I made a postal application
> weeks ago.

> TINA
> *(now sitting on the desk,*
> *scribbles on a clipboard)*
> Scamander ...
> *(finding him very fishy)*
> And you were just in
> Equatorial Guinea?

> NEWT
> I've just completed a year in
> the field. I'm writing a book
> about magical creatures.

> TINA
> Like – an extermination
> guide?

NEWT
No. A guide to help people
understand why we should
be protecting these creatures
instead of killing them.

ABERNATHY (*O.S.*)
GOLDSTEIN! Where is she?
Where is she? GOLDSTEIN!

TINA *ducks behind her desk, which amuses* NEWT.

ABERNATHY, *a pompous jobsworth, enters. He
immediately realises where* TINA *is hidden.*

ABERNATHY
Goldstein!

TINA, *looking guilty, slowly emerges from behind the desk.*

ABERNATHY
Did you just butt in on the
Investigative Team again?

TINA *is about to defend herself, but* ABERNATHY
continues.

ABERNATHY
Where've you been?

>   TINA
>   *(awkward)*
>   What ...?

>   ABERNATHY
>   *(to* NEWT*)*
>   Where'd she pick you up?

>   NEWT
>   Me?

NEWT *quickly looks at* TINA, *who shakes her head, her expression one of desperation.* NEWT *stalls – a silent pact between him and* TINA.

>   ABERNATHY
>   *(agitated by the lack of*
>   *information)*
>   Have you been tracking them
>   Second Salemers again?

>   TINA
>   Of course not, sir.

GRAVES *comes round the corner.* ABERNATHY *is immediately cowed.*

>   ABERNATHY
>   Afternoon, Mr Graves, sir!

GRAVES
Afternoon, ah – Abernathy.

TINA *steps forwards to formally address* GRAVES.

TINA
*(speaking quickly, eager to
have her case heard)*
Mr Graves, sir, this is Mr
Scamander – he has a crazy
creature in that case and it
got out and caused mayhem
in a bank, sir.

GRAVES
Let's see the little guy.

TINA *breathes a sigh of relief: finally someone is listening
to her.* NEWT *tries to speak up – he looks more panicky
than might seem warranted by a Niffler – but* GRAVES
dismisses him.

TINA *theatrically places the case onto a table and throws
open the lid. She looks aghast at the contents.*

ANGLE ON *the case contents – it is full of pastries.*
NEWT *approaches, nervous. On seeing the contents
he looks horrified.* GRAVES *looks confused, but smirks
slightly – another one of* TINA'S *mistakes.*

GRAVES

Tina ...

GRAVES *walks away.* NEWT *and* TINA *stare at each other.*

SCENE 25
EXT. STREET ON THE LOWER EAST SIDE—DAY

JACOB *marches along the overcast street, case in hand,*
past pushcarts, shabby little shops and tenement buildings.
He continually throws nervous glances over his shoulder.

SCENE 26
INT. JACOB'S ROOM—DAY

A tiny, dirty room, the furnishings sparse and shabby.

*CLOSE ON the case as JACOB throws it down onto his
bed. He looks up at a portrait of his grandmother, which
hangs on the wall.*

> JACOB
> I'm sorry, Grandma.

*JACOB sits down at his desk, hanging his head in his
hands, downcast, tired. Behind him, one of the catches on
the case flies open. JACOB turns ...*

*He sits down on the bed and examines the case. The second
catch now flicks open of its own accord, and the case begins
to shake, emitting aggressive animalistic sounds. JACOB
slowly backs away.*

*Tentatively, he leans forward ... suddenly the lid flies open
and out bursts a Murtlap – a rat-like creature with an
anemone-style growth on its back. JACOB grapples with it,
holding it tightly in both hands as it struggles.*

*We whip back to the case, which flies open once again as an
invisible being shoots out, crashing into the ceiling before
smashing through the window.*

The Murtlap lunges forwards, biting JACOB *on the neck,
sending him crashing through furniture and tumbling to
the ground.*

*The room shakes heavily, and the wall holding the picture
of* JACOB'S *grandma begins to crack before exploding, as
more creatures escape off-screen.*

SCENE 27
INT. SECOND SALEM CHURCH, MAIN HALL—
DAY—MONTAGE

*A dingy wooden church with darkened windows and a
high mezzanine balcony.* MODESTY *is playing a solitary
variation of hopscotch, skipping in and out of a chalked
grid.*

MODESTY
My momma, your momma,
gonna catch a witch
My momma, your momma,
flying on a switch
My momma, your momma,
witches never cry

My momma, your momma,
witches gonna die!

As she sings we see the church is full of group paraphernalia – leaflets advertising MARY LOU'S *campaign, and a large version of the group's anti-witchcraft banner.*

SCENE 28
INT. SECOND SALEM CHURCH, MAIN HALL—DAY

A pigeon coos from a high-up window. CREDENCE *steps forwards, staring up towards it before mechanically clapping his hands. The pigeon flies away.*

We follow CHASTITY *as she moves through the church and opens the large double doors onto the street.*

SCENE 29
EXT. SECOND SALEM CHURCH, BACKYARD—DAY

CHASTITY *emerges from the church and rings a large dinner bell.*

SCENE 30
INT. SECOND SALEM CHURCH, MAIN HALL—DAY

MODESTY *continues playing hopscotch.* CREDENCE *pauses, looking past her and out towards the door.*

> MODESTY
> Witch number three, gonna
> watch her burn,
> Witch number four, flogging
> take a turn.

Young children stream into the church.

TIME CUT:

Brown soup is being ladled out to the children, who jostle each other to get near the front of the line. MARY LOU, *wearing an apron and looking on approvingly, squeezes through the little crowd.*

> MARY LOU
> Collect your leaflets before
> you get food, children.

Several of the children turn towards CHASTITY, *who waits primly, handing out campaign leaflets.*

TIME CUT:

MARY LOU *and* CREDENCE *ladle out soup,* CREDENCE *looking intently into every face.*

A BOY *with a birthmark on his face reaches the front of the line.* CREDENCE *stops his work and stares at him.* MARY LOU *reaches out to touch the* BOY'S *face.*

> BOY
> Is it a witch's mark, ma'am?

> MARY LOU
> No. He's okay.

The BOY *takes his soup and leaves.* CREDENCE *stares after him, as they continue to serve.*

SCENE 31
EXT. MAIN STREET ON THE LOWER EAST
SIDE—AFTERNOON

*CLOSE ON a Billywig – a small blue creature with
helicopter-like wings on its head – flying high above the street.*

TINA *and* NEWT *walk along the street,* TINA *carrying the
case.*

> TINA
> *(on the verge of tears)*
> I can't *believe* you didn't
> Obliviate that man! If there's
> an inquiry I'm finished!

> NEWT
> So why would you be
> finished? I'm the one that's—

> TINA
> I'm not supposed to go near
> the Second Salemers!

The Billywig zooms over their heads. NEWT *spins,
horrified, watching it.*

> TINA
> What was that?

> NEWT
> Er – moth, I think. Big moth.

TINA *finds this explanation dubious. They round a corner to find a crowd gathered in front of a crumbling building. People are shouting, others are hurriedly evacuating the building. A* POLICEMAN *is standing at the centre of the crowd, being harassed by disgruntled tenement-dwellers.*

JUMP CUT:

NEWT *and* TINA *move around the outskirts of the crowd. At the back, a tipsy* HOBO *is trying to attract the* POLICEMAN'S *attention.*

> POLICEMAN
> Hey … hey – quiet
> down – I'm trying to get a
> statement …

> HOUSEWIFE
> … I'm telling you it's a gas
> explosion again, I ain't taking
> the kids back up there until
> it's safe.

POLICEMAN
Sorry, ma'am – there ain't no
smell of gas.

HOBO
(drunk)
It warn't gas – hey, officer,
I seen it! – it wuzza – a
gigantic – a huge hippopotto—

TINA *is looking up at the ruined building, and misses*
NEWT *sliding his wand from his sleeve and pointing it at
the* HOBO.

HOBO
—gas. It was gas.

The others in the crowd around him agree.

CROWD
Gas … it was gas!

TINA *again catches sight of the Billywig. Taking
advantage of this distraction,* NEWT *runs up the metal
steps and inside the ruined tenement building.*

SCENE 32
INT. JACOB'S ROOM—AFTERNOON

NEWT *enters* JACOB'S *room and stops, staring: the room is completely destroyed. Footprints, broken furniture, shattered glass. Even worse: a massive hole in the opposite wall – something huge has blasted its way out. We can hear* JACOB *groaning from the corner.*

SCENE 33
EXT. TENEMENT STREET—AFTERNOON

CUT BACK TO TINA *as she looks around and realises that* NEWT *has disappeared from the crowd.*

SCENE 34
INT. JACOB'S ROOM

NEWT *crouches beside* JACOB, *who lies on his back, eyes closed and moaning.* NEWT *tries to examine a small red*

bite on JACOB'S *neck, but* JACOB *keeps unconsciously batting him away.*

> TINA (O.S.)
> Mr Scamander!

CUT TO TINA, *running with purpose up the staircase of* JACOB'S *building.*

CUT BACK TO NEWT, *who desperately performs a repairing charm. The room is righted, the wall repaired, just in time before* TINA *enters the room.*

SCENE 35
INT. JACOB'S ROOM—AFTERNOON

TINA *hurries inside to find* NEWT, *trying to look innocent and composed, sitting on the bed. He calmly seals the latches on his case.*

> TINA
> It was *open?*

> NEWT
> Just a smidge ...

TINA
That crazy Niffler thing's on
the loose again?

NEWT
Er – it *might* be—

TINA
Then look for it! Look!

JACOB *moans.*

TINA *drops* JACOB'S *case and makes straight for the
injured* JACOB.

TINA
(worried about JACOB*)*
His neck's bleeding, he's hurt!
Wake up, Mr No-Maj . . .

With TINA'S *back turned,* NEWT *makes towards the door.
Suddenly,* TINA *emits a guttural scream as the Murtlap
comes scuttling out from under a cabinet and latches onto
her arm.* NEWT *spins, catching the creature by the tail and
grappling it into the case.*

TINA
Mercy Lewis, what is that?

NEWT

Nothing to worry about. That
is a Murtlap.

Unnoticed by either, JACOB *opens his eyes.*

TINA

What else have you got in
there?

JACOB
(*recognising* NEWT)

You!

NEWT

Hello.

TINA

Easy, Mr—

JACOB

Kowalski ... Jacob ...

TINA *takes* JACOB'S *hand to shake it.*

NEWT *raises his wand.* JACOB *recoils in fear, clutching at*
TINA, *who moves protectively in front of him.*

TINA

You can't Obliviate him! We
need him as a witness.

NEWT

I'm sorry – you've just yelled
at me the length of New York
for not doing it in the first
place ...

TINA

He's hurt! He looks ill!

NEWT

He'll be fine. Murtlap bites
aren't serious.

NEWT *puts his wand away.* JACOB *retches into the corner,
while* TINA *looks at* NEWT *in disbelief.*

NEWT

I admit that is a slightly more
severe reaction than I've seen,
but if it was really serious –
he'd have ...

TINA

What?

NEWT
Well, the first symptom
would be flames out of his
anus—

Terrified, JACOB *feels the seat of his pants.*

TINA
This is balled up!

NEWT
It'll last forty-eight hours at
most! I can keep him if you
want me to—

TINA
Oh, keep him? We don't
keep them! Mr Scamander,
do you know *anything* about
the wizarding community in
America?

NEWT
I do know a few things,
actually. I know you have
rather backwards laws
about relations with non-
magic people. That you're
not meant to befriend them,
that you can't marry them,

which seems mildly absurd
to me.

JACOB *is following this conversation, open-mouthed.*

> TINA
> Who's going to marry him?
> You're both coming with
> me—

> NEWT
> I don't see why I need to
> come with you—

TINA *tries to lift the partially conscious* JACOB *from the floor.*

> TINA
> Help me!

NEWT *feels obliged to help.*

> JACOB
> I'm ... I'm dreaming, right?
> Yeah ... I'm tired, I never
> went to the bank. This is
> all just some big nightmare,
> right?

TINA
For the both of us, Mr
Kowalski.

TINA *and* NEWT *Disapparate with* JACOB.

We focus on the photo of JACOB'S *grandma, once again hanging on the wall. Eventually the photo gives a little shake before falling and revealing a hole in the wall, inhabited by the Niffler.*

SCENE 36
EXT. UPPER EAST SIDE—AFTERNOON

*A young boy, clutching a huge lollipop, is led down the busy
street by his father. As they pass a fruit barrow, an apple
suddenly levitates, bobbing along beside him. The boy gazes
in wonder as the apple is eaten by something invisible,
then the smile fades as his lollipop is snatched by the same
unseen hands.*

*At a newsstand, the eyes of a lady on an advertisement
blink open. The outline of a creature becomes visible,
camouflage-like, before it peels away from the poster. It
moves along the street, invisible again, only locatable by the
lollipop it holds – seemingly suspended in mid-air. A dog*

barks in its direction, and the creature scuttles on, knocking over newspaper stands, causing bikes and cars to swerve.

ANGLE ON the roof of a department store – we see a thin blue tail slither inside a small attic window. Suddenly the building shakes and tiles break away, as the creature's size expands to fill the whole room.

SCENE 37
INT. SHAW TOWER NEWSROOM—DUSK

The glittering Art Deco headquarters of a media empire. Many journalists are hard at work in an outer office.

An elevator opens and LANGDON SHAW *bustles excitedly through the room, leading the Second Salemers. He carries maps, several old books and a handful of photographs.*

MARY LOU *is composed,* CHASTITY *looks shy and* MODESTY *is excited, curious.* CREDENCE *looks nervous – he doesn't like crowds.*

> LANGDON
> … and so this is the
> newsroom.

LANGDON *spins around excitedly, eager to show the Second Salemers that he holds authority here.*

> LANGDON
> Let's go!

LANGDON *moves around the office and speaks to some of the workers.*

> LANGDON
> Hey, how are you? Make
> way for the Barebones! Now,
> they're just putting the papers
> to bed, as they say.

Looks of veiled amusement from journalists as LANGDON *leads his group to double doors at the end of the open-plan area.* HENRY SHAW SR'S *assistant –* BARKER *– stands up, anxious.*

> BARKER
> Mr Shaw, sir, he's with the
> senator—

> LANGDON
> Never mind that, Barker, I
> wanna see my father!

LANGDON *pushes past.*

SCENE 38
INT. SHAW SR'S PENTHOUSE OFFICE—DUSK

A large, impressive office with spectacular views across the city. The newspaper magnate – HENRY SHAW SR – is talking to his elder son, SENATOR SHAW.

> SENATOR SHAW
> ... we could just buy the
> boats ...

The doors burst open to reveal a harassed-looking BARKER and an excitable LANGDON.

> BARKER
> I'm so sorry, Mr Shaw, but
> your son insisted—

> LANGDON
> Father, you're going to want
> to hear this.

LANGDON moves towards his father's desk and begins spreading out photographs. We recognise some of the images: the destroyed streets from the start of the film.

LANGDON
I've got something huge!

SHAW SR
Your brother and I are busy
here, Langdon. Working on
his campaign. We don't have
time for this.

MARY LOU, CREDENCE, CHASTITY *and* MODESTY
enter the office. SHAW SR *and* SENATOR SHAW *stare.*
CREDENCE *stands with his head bowed, embarrassed,*
nervous.

LANGDON
This is Mary Lou Barebone
from the New Salem
Philanthropic Society, and
she's got a big story for you!

SHAW SR
Oh she has – has she?

LANGDON
There's strange things going
on all over the city. The
people behind this – they are
not like you and me. This is
witchcraft, don't you see?

SHAW SR *and the* SENATOR *look dubious – all too used to* LANGDON'S *harebrained little projects and interests.*

> SHAW SR
> Langdon.

> LANGDON
> She doesn't want any money.

> SHAW SR
> Then either her story is
> worthless, or she's lying about
> the cost. Nobody gives away
> anything valuable for free.

> MARY LOU
> *(confident, persuasive)*
> You are right, Mr Shaw. What
> we desire is infinitely more
> valuable than money: it's your
> influence. Millions of people
> read your newspapers and
> they need to be made aware
> about this danger.

> LANGDON
> The crazy disturbances in
> the subway – just look at the
> pictures!

SHAW SR
I'd like you and your friends
to leave.

LANGDON
No, you're missing a
trick here. Just look at the
evidence—

SHAW SR
Really.

SENATOR SHAW
*(joining his father
and brother)*
Langdon. Just listen to Father
and go.

His eyes shift, focus on CREDENCE.

SENATOR SHAW
And take the freaks with you.

CREDENCE *perceptibly twitches, disturbed by anger in his*
vicinity. MARY LOU *is calm, but steely.*

LANGDON
This is Father's office, not
yours, and I'm sick of this
every time I walk in here …

SHAW SR *silences his son and motions for the*
BAREBONES *to leave.*

> SHAW SR
> That's it – thank you.

> MARY LOU
> *(calm, dignified)*
> We hope you'll reconsider,
> Mr Shaw. We're not difficult
> to find. Until then, we thank
> you for your time.

SHAW SR *and* SENATOR SHAW *watch* MARY LOU *as
she turns, leading her children out. The newsroom has
fallen quiet, everyone craning to hear the row.*

As he departs, CREDENCE *drops a leaflet.* SENATOR
SHAW *moves forwards and bends to pick it up. He glances
at the witches on the front.*

> SENATOR SHAW
> *(to* CREDENCE*)*
> Hey, boy. You dropped
> something.

The SENATOR *crumples up the leaflet before putting it in*
CREDENCE'S *hand.*

SENATOR SHAW
Here you go, freak – why
don't you put that in the trash
where you all belong.

Behind CREDENCE, MODESTY'S *eyes burn. She clutches*
CREDENCE'S *hand protectively.*

SCENE 39
EXT. BROWNSTONE STREET—SHORTLY
AFTERWARDS—DUSK

TINA *and* NEWT *stand on either side of an ailing* JACOB,
trying to keep him steady.

TINA
Take a right here …

JACOB *makes various retching sounds, the bite on his neck*
clearly affecting him more and more.

As the group rounds a corner, TINA *hurries them to hide*
behind a large repair truck. From here she peers at a house
across the street.

TINA
Okay – before we go in – I'm
not supposed to have men on
the premises.

NEWT
In that case, Mr Kowalski
and I can easily seek other
accommodation—

TINA
Oh no, you don't!

TINA *quickly grabs* JACOB'S *arm and pulls him across the road,* NEWT *dutifully following.*

TINA
Watch your step.

SCENE 40
INT. GOLDSTEIN RESIDENCE, STAIRWELL—DUSK

NEWT, TINA *and* JACOB *tiptoe up the stairs. They have just reached the first landing when* MRS ESPOSITO, *the landlady, calls out. The group freezes.*

> MRS ESPOSITO (*O.S.*)
> That you, Tina?

> TINA
> Yes, Mrs Esposito!

> MRS ESPOSITO (*O.S.*)
> Are you alone?

> TINA
> I'm always alone, Mrs Esposito!

A beat.

SCENE 41
INT. GOLDSTEIN RESIDENCE, SITTING ROOM—DUSK

The group enters the Goldstein apartment.

Although impoverished, the apartment is enlivened by workaday magic. An iron is working away on its own in a corner, and a clothes horse revolves clumsily on its wooden legs in front of the fire, drying an assortment of underwear. Magazines are scattered around: The

Witch's Friend, Witch Chat *and* Transfiguration Today.

Blonde QUEENIE, *the most beautiful girl ever to don witches' robes, is standing in a silk slip, supervising the mending of a dress on a dressmaker's dummy.* JACOB *is thunderstruck.*

NEWT *barely notices. Impatient to leave as soon as possible, he starts peeking out of the windows.*

> QUEENIE
> Teenie – you brought men home?

> TINA
> Gentlemen, this is my sister.
> You want to put something on, Queenie?

> QUEENIE
> *(unconcerned)*
> Oh, sure—

She runs her wand up the dummy and the dress runs magically up her body. JACOB *watches the display, dumbfounded.*

TINA, *frustrated, starts tidying the apartment.*

QUEENIE
So, who are they?

TINA
That's Mr Scamander.
He's committed a serious
infraction of the National
Statute of Secrecy—

QUEENIE
(*impressed*)
He's a *criminal*?

TINA
—uh huh, and this is Mr
Kowalski, he's a No-Maj—

QUEENIE
(*suddenly worried*)
A No-Maj? Teen – what are
you up to?

TINA
He's sick – it's a long story –
Mr Scamander has lost
something, I'm going to help
him find it.

JACOB *suddenly staggers, very sweaty and unwell.*
QUEENIE *runs to him as* TINA *hovers, also worried.*

QUEENIE
(*as* JACOB *falls back onto
a sofa*)
You need to sit down, honey.
Hey—
(*reading his mind*)
—he hasn't eaten all day.
And—
(*reading his mind*)
—aww, that's rough,
(*reading his mind*)
—he didn't get the money he
wanted for his bakery. You
bake, honey? I love to cook.

NEWT *is watching* QUEENIE *from his spot by the
window, his scientific attention now aroused.*

NEWT
You're a Legilimens?

QUEENIE
Uh huh, yeah. But I always
have trouble with your kind.
Brits. It's the accent.

JACOB
(*cottoning on, appalled*)
You know how to read minds?

QUEENIE
Aww, don't worry, honey.
Most guys think what you was
thinking, first time they see me.

QUEENIE *playfully gestures towards* JACOB *with her wand.*

QUEENIE
Now, you need food.

NEWT *looks out the window and sees a Billywig fly past –
he's nervous, impatient to get out and find his creatures.*

TINA *and* QUEENIE *busy themselves in the kitchen.
Ingredients come floating out of cupboards as* QUEENIE
*enchants them into the components of a meal – carrots and
apples chop themselves, pastry rolls itself and pans stir.*

QUEENIE
(*to* TINA)
Hot dog ... again?

TINA
Don't read my mind!

QUEENIE
Not a very wholesome lunch.

TINA *points her wand at the cupboards. Dishes, assorted
cutlery and glasses come flying out, setting themselves on*

the table with a little prodding from TINA'S *wand.* JACOB, *half-fascinated, half-terrified, staggers towards the table.*

ANGLE ON NEWT, *his hand on the doorknob.*

> QUEENIE
> *(artless)*
> Hey, Mr Scamander, you
> prefer pie or strudel?

All look at NEWT *who, embarrassed, removes his hand from the doorknob.*

> NEWT
> I really don't have a
> preference.

TINA *stares at* NEWT: *confrontational, but also disappointed and hurt.*

JACOB *is already seated at the table, tucking his napkin into his shirt.*

> QUEENIE
> *(reading* JACOB'S *mind)*
> You prefer strudel, huh,
> honey? Strudel it is.

JACOB *nods with excited enthusiasm.* QUEENIE *grins back, delighted.*

With a flick of her wand, QUEENIE *sends raisins, apples and pastry flying into the air. The concoction neatly wraps itself up into a cylindrical pie, baking on the spot, complete with ornate decoration and a dusting of sugar.* JACOB *takes a deep breath in: heaven.*

TINA *lights candles on the table – the meal is ready.*

FOCUS ON NEWT'S *pocket, a small squeak, and* PICKETT *pokes his head out, curious.*

> TINA
> Well, sit down, Mr
> Scamander, we're not going
> to poison you.

NEWT, *still hovering near the door, looks somewhat charmed by the situation.* JACOB *glares at him subtly, willing him to sit down.*

SCENE 42
EXT. BROADWAY—NIGHT

CREDENCE *is walking alone through a worldly crowd of late-night diners and theatre-goers. Traffic roars past. He is trying to give out leaflets but is met with only incredulity and faint derision.*

The Woolworth Building looms ahead. CREDENCE *glances towards it with a hint of longing.* GRAVES *stands outside, watching* CREDENCE *intently.* CREDENCE *spots*

him, hope flickering across his face. Utterly enthralled,
CREDENCE *moves across the street towards* GRAVES,
barely looking where he's going – everything else is
forgotten.

SCENE 43
EXT. ALLEYWAY—NIGHT

CREDENCE *stands, head bowed, at the end of a dimly*
lit alleyway. GRAVES *joins him, moving in very close to*
whisper, conspiratorial:

> GRAVES
> You're upset. It's your mother
> again. Somebody's said
> something – what did they
> say? Tell me.

> CREDENCE
> Do you think I'm a freak?

> GRAVES
> No – I think you're a very
> special young man or I
> wouldn't have asked you to
> help me now, would I?

A pause. GRAVES *rests a hand on* CREDENCE'S *arm.*
The human contact seems to both startle and captivate
CREDENCE.

> GRAVES
> Have you any news?

> CREDENCE
> I'm still looking. Mr Graves,
> if I knew whether it was a girl
> or boy—

> GRAVES
> My vision showed only the
> child's immense power. He
> or she is no older than ten,
> and I saw this child in close
> proximity to your mother –
> she I saw so plainly.

> CREDENCE
> That could be any one of
> hundreds.

GRAVES'S *tone softens – he's beguiling, comforting.*

> GRAVES
> There is something else.
> Something I haven't told you.
> I saw you beside me in New

York. You're the one that
gains this child's trust. You
are the key – I saw this. You
want to join the wizarding
world. I want those things
too, Credence. I want them
for you. So find the child.
Find the child and we'll all be
free.

SCENE 44
INT. GOLDSTEIN RESIDENCE, SITTING ROOM—HALF AN HOUR LATER—NIGHT

The catch on NEWT'S *case pops open.* NEWT *reaches down and pushes it shut.*

JACOB *looks a little better for having eaten. He and* QUEENIE *are getting on famously.*

> QUEENIE
> The job ain't that glamorous.
> I mean, I spend most days
> making coffee, unjinxing the
> john ... Tina's the career girl.

(she reads his mind)
Nah. We're orphans. Ma and
Pa died of dragon pox when
we were kids. Aww ...
(reading his mind)
You're sweet. But we got each
other!

JACOB
Could you stop reading my
mind for a second? Don't get
me wrong – I love it.

QUEENIE giggles, delighted, captivated by JACOB.

JACOB
This meal – it's insanely
good! This is what I do – I'm
a cook and this is, like, the
greatest meal I have ever had
in my life.

QUEENIE
(laughing)
Oh you slay me! I ain't never
really talked to a No-Maj
before.

JACOB
Really?

QUEENIE *and* JACOB *gaze into each other's eyes.* NEWT *and* TINA *sit opposite each other, uncomfortably silent in the presence of such affectionate behaviour.*

> QUEENIE
> (*to* TINA)
> I am not flirting!

> TINA
> (*embarrassed*)
> I'm just saying – don't go
> getting attached, he's going to
> have to be Obliviated!
> (*to* JACOB)
> It's nothing personal.

JACOB *is suddenly very pale and sweaty again, although still trying to look good for* QUEENIE.

> QUEENIE
> (*to* JACOB)
> Oh, hey, you okay, honey?

NEWT *briskly gets up from the table and awkwardly stands behind his chair.*

> NEWT
> Miss Goldstein, I think Mr
> Kowalski could do with an
> early night. And besides, you

and I will need to be up early
tomorrow morning to find
my Niffler, so—

> QUEENIE
> (*to* TINA)
> What's a Niffler?

TINA *looks put out.*

> TINA
> Don't ask.
> (*moving towards a back room*)
> Okay, you guys can bunk in
> here.

SCENE 45
INT. GOLDSTEIN RESIDENCE, BEDROOM—
NIGHT

The boys are tucked up in neatly made twin beds. NEWT *is
resolutely turned away on his side, while* JACOB *is sitting
up in bed, trying to make sense of a wizarding book.*

TINA, *wearing patterned blue pyjamas, tentatively knocks*

on the door, and enters carrying a tray of cocoa. The mugs
are stirring themselves – JACOB is captivated again.

> TINA
> I thought you might like a hot
> drink?

TINA carefully hands JACOB his mug. NEWT remains
turned away, feigning sleep, so TINA, with some
frustration, pointedly places his cup on the bedside table.

> JACOB
> Hey, Mr Scamander—
>> *(to NEWT, trying to make*
>> *him friendlier)*
> Look, cocoa!

NEWT does not move.

> TINA
>> *(irritated)*
> The toilet's down the hall to
> the right.

> JACOB
> Thanks ...

As TINA shuts the door, JACOB gets a quick glimpse of
QUEENIE in the other room, wearing a much less demure
dressing gown.

> JACOB

Very much ...

The moment the door closes NEWT *jumps up, still wearing
his overcoat, and places his case on the floor. To* JACOB'S
utter astonishment, NEWT *opens the case and walks down
inside it, now completely out of sight.*

JACOB *lets out a small scream of alarm.*

NEWT'S *hand appears from the case, beckoning him
imperiously.* JACOB *stares, breathing heavily, trying to
process the situation.*

NEWT'S *hand, impatient, appears again.*

> NEWT (*O.S.*)

Come on.

JACOB *rallies himself, gets out of bed and steps down into*
NEWT'S *case. However, he gets stuck at his waistline and
tries hard to squeeze himself through, the case bouncing up
and down with his efforts.*

> JACOB

For the love of ...

With a final frustrated jump, JACOB *suddenly disappears
through the case, which snaps shut after him.*

SCENE 46
INT. NEWT'S CASE—A MOMENT LATER—NIGHT

JACOB *crashes down the steps of the case, colliding with various objects, instruments and bottles as he goes.*

He finds himself inside a small wooden shed containing a camp bed, tropical gear and various tools hung up on the walls. Wooden cupboards contain rope, nets and collecting jars. A very old typewriter, a pile of manuscripts and a medieval bestiary sit on a desk. Potted plants line a shelf. Rows of pills and tablets, syringes and vials form a medicine chest, and tacked up on the walls are notes, maps, drawings and a few moving photographs of extraordinary creatures. A dried carcass hangs from a hook. Several sacks of feed are resting against the wall.

> NEWT
> *(glances at* JACOB*)*
> Will you sit down.

JACOB *drops onto a crate hand-labelled MOONCALF PELLETS.*

> JACOB
> That's good.

NEWT *moves forward to examine the bite on* JACOB'S *neck – one quick glance.*

> NEWT
> Ah, that's definitely the Murtlap.
> You must be particularly
> susceptible. See, you're a
> Muggle. So our physiologies are
> subtly different.

NEWT *busies himself at his work station, using plants and the contents of various bottles to create a poultice, which he rapidly applies to* JACOB'S *neck.*

> JACOB
> Oww …

NEWT
Now stay still. Now that
should stop the sweating.
(handing him some pills)
And one of those should sort
the twitch.

JACOB looks suspiciously at the pills in his hand. Finally,
deciding he has nothing to lose, he swallows them.

ANGLE ON NEWT, who has now removed his waistcoat,
undone his bow tie and lowered his braces. He picks up a
meat cleaver and hacks chunks of meat off a large carcass,
before tossing them into a bucket.

NEWT
(handing him the bucket)
Take that.

JACOB looks disgusted. NEWT doesn't notice, his attention
now focused on a spiny cocoon, which he slowly begins to
squeeze. As he does so, the cocoon emits a luminous venom,
which NEWT collects into a glass vial.

NEWT
(to the cocoon)
Come on . . .

JACOB
What you got there?

> NEWT
> Well this – the locals call
> 'Swooping Evil' – not the
> friendliest of names. It's quite
> an agile fellow.

As if to demonstrate, NEWT *flicks the cocoon, which unravels, dangling elegantly from his finger.*

> NEWT
> I've been studying him.
> And I am pretty sure his
> venom could be quite useful
> if properly diluted. Just to
> remove bad memories, you
> know.

Quite suddenly NEWT *throws the Swooping Evil towards* JACOB. *The creature bursts out from its cocoon – a bat-like, spikey and colourful creature – which howls in* JACOB'S *face before* NEWT *recalls it.* JACOB *recoils dramatically, but this was evidently* NEWT'S *idea of a little joke ...*

> NEWT
> *(smiling to himself)*
> Probably shouldn't let him
> loose in here, though.

NEWT *opens the door of his shed and walks through.*

NEWT

Come on.

JACOB, *now thoroughly startled, follows him out.*

SCENE 47
INT. NEWT'S CASE, ANIMAL AREA—DAY

The perimeter of the leather case is dimly visible, but the place has swollen to the size of a small aircraft hangar. It contains what appears to be a safari park in miniature. Each of NEWT'S creatures has its own perfect, magically realised, habitat.

JACOB *steps into this world, totally amazed.*

NEWT *is standing in the nearest habitat – a slice of Arizona desert. This area contains FRANK, a magnificent Thunderbird – a creature like a large albatross, his glorious wings shimmering with cloud- and sun-like patterns. One of his legs is rubbed raw and bloody – he has obviously previously been chained. As FRANK flaps his wings, his habitat fills with a torrential downpour, thunder and lightning. NEWT uses his wand to create a magical umbrella, shielding him from the rain.*

> NEWT
> *(eyes on* FRANK *up high)*
> Come on ... come on ...
> down you come ... come on.

Slowly FRANK *calms himself, lowering down to stand on a large rock in front of* NEWT. *As he does, the rain dies down and is replaced by a brilliant, hot sunshine.*

NEWT *puts his wand away and produces a handful of grubs from his pocket.* FRANK *watches intently.*

NEWT *strokes* FRANK *with his free hand, calming him, affectionate.*

> NEWT
> Oh, thank Paracelsus. If you'd
> have got out that could have
> been quite catastrophic.
> *(to* JACOB)
> You see, he's the real reason
> I came to America. To bring
> Frank home.

JACOB, *still staring, steps slowly forwards. In reaction,* FRANK *starts to flap his wings, agitated.*

> NEWT
> *(to* JACOB)
> No sorry – stay there – he's a

wee bit sensitive to strangers.
(*to* FRANK, *calming*)
Here you are – here you are.
(*to* JACOB)
He was trafficked, you see. I
found him in Egypt, he was
all chained up. Couldn't leave
him there, had to bring him
back. I'm going to put you
back where you belong, aren't
I, Frank. To the wilds of
Arizona.

NEWT, *his face full of hope and expectation, hugs*
FRANK'S *head. Then, grinning, he casts the handful of
grubs high into the air.* FRANK *soars majestically upwards
after them, sunlight bursting from his wings.*

NEWT *watches him fly with love and pride. Then he turns,
puts his hands to his mouth, and roars beast-like towards
another area of the case.*

NEWT *moves past* JACOB, *grabbing the bucket of meat.*
JACOB *stumbles after him as several Doxys buzz around
his head.* JACOB, *dazed, swats them out of the way. Behind
him a large dung beetle rolls a giant ball of dung.*

We hear NEWT *roar loudly again.* JACOB *hurries towards
the sound, finding* NEWT *in a sandy, moonlit territory.*

> NEWT
> (under his breath)
Ah – here they come.

> JACOB
Here who comes?

> NEWT
The Graphorns.

*A large creature comes charging into sight: a Graphorn –
built like a sabre-toothed tiger but with slimy tentacles at
its mouth.* JACOB *screams and tries to back off, but* NEWT
grabs hold of his arm, stopping him.

> NEWT
You're all right. You're all
right.

The Graphorn moves closer to NEWT.

> NEWT
> (stroking the Graphorn)
Hello, hello!

The Graphorn's strange slimy tentacles rest on NEWT'S
shoulder, seeming to embrace him.

> NEWT
So they're the last breeding

pair in existence. If I hadn't
managed to rescue them, that
could have been the end of
Graphorns – for ever.

A younger Graphorn trots straight up to JACOB *and begins
licking his hand, circling him curiously. He stares down
at it, then gently reaches out and strokes its head.* NEWT
watches JACOB, *pleased.*

>   NEWT
> All right.

NEWT *throws a piece of meat into the enclosure, which is
hastily chased and consumed by the young Graphorn.*

>   JACOB
> So what – you, you rescue
> these creatures?

>   NEWT
> Yes, that's right. Rescue,
> nurture and protect them, and
> I'm gently trying to educate my
> fellow wizards about them.

*A tiny bright pink bird, the Fwooper, flies past and comes to
rest on a little perch, suspended from mid-air.*

NEWT *heads up a small ramp of stairs.*

NEWT
(to JACOB)

Come on.

They enter a bamboo wood, ducking and diving through the trees. NEWT *calls out.*

NEWT

Titus? Finn? Poppy, Marlow, Tom?

They emerge into a sunlit glade, NEWT *producing* PICKETT *from his pocket and holding him perched on his hand.*

NEWT
(to JACOB)

He had a cold. He needed some body warmth.

JACOB

Aww.

They move towards a small tree bathed in sunlight. At their approach, a clan of Bowtruckles chatters and rushes out of the leaves.

NEWT *extends his arm towards the tree, trying to persuade* PICKETT *to rejoin the others. The Bowtruckles clack noisily when they see* PICKETT.

NEWT
Right, on you hop.

PICKETT *steadfastly refuses to leave* NEWT'S *arm.*

NEWT
(*to* JACOB)
See, he has some attachment
issues.
(*to* PICKETT)
Now come on, Pickett. Pickett.
No, they're not going to bully
you … now, come on. Pickett!

PICKETT *clings by his spindly hands to one of* NEWT'S
fingers, desperate not to return to the tree. NEWT *finally
resigns himself.*

NEWT
All right. But that is exactly
why they accuse me of
favouritism …

NEWT *puts* PICKETT *onto his shoulder and turns. On
seeing a large, round, empty nest, he looks concerned.*

NEWT
I wonder where Dougal's gone.

From within a nearby nest, we hear chirping sounds.

> NEWT
> All right I'm coming ... I'm
> coming, Mum's here – Mum's
> here.

NEWT *reaches into the nest and scoops up a baby Occamy.*

> NEWT
> Ah – hello you – let me take a
> look at you.

> JACOB
> I know these guys.

> NEWT
> New Occamy.
>> (*to* JACOB)
> Your Occamy.

> JACOB
> What do you mean? My
> Occamy?

> NEWT
> Yes – do you want to ...

NEWT *proffers the Occamy to* JACOB.

JACOB
Oh wow ... yeah, sure.
Okay ... ah ha.

JACOB *holds the newborn creature gently in his hands and stares. As he moves to stroke its head, the Occamy moves to nip him.* JACOB *starts backwards.*

NEWT
Ah, no, sorry – don't pet
them. They learn to defend
themselves early. See, their
shells are made of silver so
they're incredibly valuable.

NEWT *feeds the other babies in the nest.*

JACOB
Okay ...

NEWT
Their nests tend to get
ransacked by hunters.

NEWT, *delighted by* JACOB'S *interest in his creatures, takes back the baby Occamy, placing it in the nest.*

JACOB
Thank you.
            (croaky)
Mr Scamander?

NEWT
Call me Newt.

JACOB
Newt ... I don't think I'm
dreaming.

NEWT
(vaguely amused)
What gave it away?

JACOB
I ain't got the brains to make
this up.

NEWT *looks at* JACOB, *both intrigued and flattered.*

NEWT
Actually, would you
mind throwing some of
those pellets in with the
Mooncalves over there?

JACOB
Yeah, sure.

JACOB *bends down and picks up the bucket of pellets.*

NEWT
Just over there ...

NEWT *grabs a nearby wheelbarrow and sets off further into the case.*

> NEWT
> *(annoyed)*
> Bugger – the Niffler's gone.
> Of course he has, little
> bugger. Any chance to get his
> hands on something shiny.

As JACOB *walks through the case, we see what appear to be golden 'leaves' falling from a tiny tree, which move together en masse towards the camera. They swarm upwards, mingling with Doxys, Glow Bugs and Grindylows which float through the air.*

THE CAMERA PANS UP to reveal another magnificent creature, the Nundu – looking almost exactly like a lion, it has a large mane which bursts forth when it roars. It stands proudly on a large rock, roaring at the moon. NEWT *scatters food at its feet and purposefully moves on.*

A Diricawl – a small, plump bird – waddles in the foreground followed by its constantly Apparating chicks, as JACOB *climbs up a steep grassy bank.*

> JACOB
> *(to himself)*
> What did you do today,
> Jacob? I was inside a suitcase.

At the top, JACOB *finds a large moonlit rock face populated by little Mooncalves – shy, with huge eyes filling their whole faces.*

> JACOB
> Hey! Oh, hello fellas – all
> right – all right.

The Mooncalves jump and hop down the rocks towards JACOB, *who finds himself suddenly surrounded by their friendly, hopeful faces.*

> JACOB
> Take it easy – take it easy.

As he throws pellets, the Mooncalves bob eagerly up and down. JACOB *visibly seems to be feeling better – he really likes this ...*

ANGLE ON NEWT, *now cradling a luminescent creature with sprouting alien-like tendrils. He feeds the creature with a bottle, while carefully watching how* JACOB *handles the Mooncalves – he recognises a kindred spirit.*

> JACOB
> (still feeding the
> Mooncalves)
> There you go, cutie. Ah, there
> it is.

A kind of icy cry echoes from nearby.

> JACOB
> (*towards* NEWT)
> Did you hear that?

But NEWT *is gone.* JACOB *turns to see a curtain billowing open, behind which is revealed a snowscape.*

We push inwards, towards a small oleaginous black mass suspended in mid-air – an Obscurus. JACOB, *intrigued, moves into the snowscape to get a closer look. The mass continues to swirl, emitting a disturbed, restless energy.* JACOB *reaches out to touch it.*

> NEWT (*O.S.*)
> (*sharp*)
> Step back.

JACOB *jumps.*

> JACOB
> Jeez …

> NEWT
> Step back …

> JACOB
> What's the matter with this?

NEWT

I said step away.

JACOB

What the hell is this thing?

NEWT

It's an Obscurus.

JACOB *looks at* NEWT, *who is momentarily lost in a
bad reverie.* NEWT *turns abruptly away and heads back
towards the hut, his tone colder, more efficient, no longer
happy to play about in the case.*

NEWT

I need to get going, find
everyone who's escaped
before they get hurt.

The pair enters another forest, NEWT *ploughing ahead, on
a mission.*

JACOB

Before *they* could get hurt?

NEWT

Yes, Mr Kowalski. See,
they're currently in alien
terrain, surrounded by
millions of the most vicious
creatures on the planet.

(a beat)

Humans.

NEWT *stops once more, staring into a large savannah
enclosure, which is empty of any beasts.*

NEWT

So where would you say that
a medium-sized creature that
likes broad, open plains –
trees – water holes – that kind
of thing – where might she
go?

JACOB

In New York City?

NEWT

Yes.

JACOB

Plains?

JACOB *shrugs as he tries to think of somewhere.*

JACOB

Ah – Central Park?

NEWT

And where is that exactly?

JACOB
Where is Central Park?

A beat.

JACOB
Well look, I would come and
show you, but, don't you
think it's kind of a double
cross? The girls take us in –
they make us hot cocoa …

NEWT
You do realise that when they
see you've stopped sweating,
they'll Obliviate you in a
heartbeat.

JACOB
What does 'Bliviate' mean?

NEWT
It'll be like you wake up and
all memory of magic is gone.

JACOB
I won't remember any of this?

He looks around. This world is extraordinary.

NEWT

No.

JACOB

All right, yeah – okay – I'll
help you.

NEWT
(picking up a bucket)
Come on, then.

SCENE 48
EXT./INT. STREET OUTSIDE SECOND SALEM
CHURCH—NIGHT

CREDENCE *walks home towards the church. He looks happier than before: his meeting with* GRAVES *has comforted him.*

CREDENCE *slowly enters the church, shutting the double doors quietly.*

CHASTITY *is in the kitchen area, drying crockery.*

MARY LOU *sits in semi-darkness on the stairs.*
CREDENCE *senses her and pauses, his face one of*
trepidation.

> MARY LOU
> Credence – where have you
> been?

> CREDENCE
> I was ... looking for a place
> for tomorrow's meeting.
> There's a corner on Thirty-
> second that could—

CREDENCE *moves round to the bottom of the stairs,*
falling silent at the severe expression on MARY LOU'S
face.

> CREDENCE
> I'm sorry, Ma. I didn't realise
> it was so late.

As if on autopilot, CREDENCE *removes his belt.* MARY
LOU *stands and extends her hand, taking the belt. In*
silence, she turns and walks up the stairs, CREDENCE
obediently following.

MODESTY *moves to the bottom of the stairs, watching*
them go, a look of fear and upset on her face.

SCENE 49
EXT. CENTRAL PARK—NIGHT

*A large frozen pond in the middle of Central Park.
Children ice-skate. A boy takes a tumble. A girl comes to
help him up, they link hands.*

*As they are about to stand, a light becomes visible
underneath the ice. A deep rumbling sound echoes. The
children stare as a glowing beast glides under the ice
beneath them, and off into the distance.*

SCENE 50
EXT. DIAMOND DISTRICT—NIGHT

NEWT *and* JACOB *walk along another deserted street
on the way to Central Park. The shops around them are
full of expensive jewellery, diamonds, precious stones.*
NEWT, *carrying his case, scans the shadows for small
movements.*

NEWT

I was watching you at dinner.

JACOB

Yeah.

NEWT

People like you, don't they,
Mr Kowalski.

JACOB
(startled)
Oh – well, I'm – I'm sure
people like you, too – huh?

NEWT
(not very concerned)
No, not really. I annoy
people.

JACOB
(not sure how to answer)
Ah.

NEWT *seems thoroughly intrigued by* JACOB.

NEWT

Why did you decide to be a
baker?

JACOB

Ah, well, um – because I'm
dying – in that canning
factory.
    (*off* NEWT'S *look*)
Everyone there's dying. It
just crushes the life outta you.
You like canned food?

NEWT

No.

JACOB

Me neither. That's why I
want to make pastries, you
know. It makes people happy.
We're going this way.

JACOB *heads off to his right.* NEWT *follows.*

NEWT

So did you get your loan?

JACOB

Er, no – I ain't got no collateral.
Stayed in the army too long,
apparently – I don't know.

NEWT

What, you fought in the war?

JACOB
Of course I fought in the war,
everyone fought in the war –
you didn't fight in the war?

NEWT
I worked mostly with
dragons, Ukrainian
Ironbellies – Eastern Front.

NEWT *suddenly stops. He has noticed a small shiny earring lying on top of a car bonnet. His eyes move downwards: diamonds are scattered across the pavement, leading towards the window of one particular diamond shop.*

NEWT *stealthily follows the trail, creeping past shop windows. Something catches his eye and suddenly he pauses. Very slowly, he tiptoes backwards.*

The Niffler is standing in a shop window. In order to hide, it is emulating a jewellery stand, little arms outstretched, covered in diamonds.

NEWT *stares at the Niffler in disbelief. Sensing* NEWT'S *stare, the Niffler slowly turns. The two of them make eye contact.*

A beat.

*Suddenly the Niffler is off: scurrying further into the shop
and away from* NEWT. NEWT *whips out his wand.*

NEWT

Finestra.

The window glass shatters and NEWT *leaps inside, seizing
at drawers and cupboards, desperate to find the creature.*
JACOB *stares down the street, incredulous as he watches*
NEWT *who, from an outsider's perspective, appears to be
looting the diamond shop.*

The Niffler appears, scurrying over NEWT'S *shoulders
in an attempt to get higher and away from his clutches.*
NEWT *jumps onto a desk after him, but the Niffler is now
balancing on a crystal chandelier.*

NEWT *reaches out and trips, both he and the Niffler now
hanging from the chandelier as it swings wildly round and
round.*

JACOB *looks around the street nervously, checking if anyone
else can hear the chaos coming from within the shop.*

*Finally the chandelier crashes to the floor, smashing.
Straight away the Niffler is back up, clambering across
cases full of jewellery,* NEWT *in hot pursuit.*

A catch opens on NEWT'S *case and a roar comes from
within.* JACOB *fearfully looks towards the case.*

The Niffler and NEWT *continue their chase, finally climbing onto a jewellery case that can't take their weight. The case, with them both on top, falls to rest against one of the shop windows. Both* NEWT *and the Niffler become very still . . .*

JACOB *breathes deeply and slowly moves forward to close the latch on the case.*

Suddenly a crack appears on the window. NEWT *watches as the crack spreads across the pane of glass and the window bursts open, shattering across the pavement –* NEWT *and the Niffler crashing to the ground.*

The Niffler is still only for a moment before running off down the street. NEWT *quickly gathers himself, drawing his wand.*

NEWT

ACCIO!

IN SLOW MOTION the Niffler sails backwards through the air towards NEWT. *As he flies, he looks sideways at the most glorious window display yet. His eyes widen. Jewellery falls from his pouch as he flies towards* NEWT *and* JACOB, *who duck and dive as they run forwards towards the creature.*

Passing a lamp-post, the Niffler stretches out an arm, spinning around the pole and flying onwards, out of the trajectory

NEWT *had him on, and towards the glorious window.*
NEWT *casts a spell towards the window, turning it into a*
sticky jelly, which finally traps the Niffler.

NEWT
(to the Niffler)
All right? Happy?

NEWT, *now covered in jewellery, pulls the Niffler from the*
window.

We hear police sirens in the background.

NEWT
One down, two to go.

Police cars come racing through the streets.

NEWT *once again sets about shaking all the diamonds*
from the Niffler's pocket.

The police cars pull up, and POLICEMEN *run out, guns*
aimed at NEWT *and* JACOB. JACOB, *also covered in*
jewels, holds up his hands in surrender.

JACOB
They went that way, officer …

POLICE OFFICER 1
Hands up!

The Niffler, stuffed into NEWT'S *overcoat, pokes out its little nose and squeaks.*

POLICE OFFICER 2
What the hell is THAT?

JACOB *suddenly looks to the left, his face one of terror.*

JACOB
(barely able to speak)
Lion ...

A beat and then, in unison, the police turn both their eyes and their guns towards the other end of the street.

Perplexed, NEWT *looks too ... a lion is stalking towards them.*

NEWT
(calm)
You know, New York is
considerably more interesting
than I'd expected.

Before the police can look back, NEWT *grabs* JACOB *and they Disapparate.*

SCENE 51
EXT. CENTRAL PARK—NIGHT

NEWT *and* JACOB *hurry through the frost-covered park.*

As they cross a bridge, they are almost bowled over by an ostrich, which tears past them, running for its life.

A loud rumble can be heard in the distance.

NEWT *tugs protective headgear out of his pocket, and hands it to* JACOB.

> NEWT
> Put this on.

> JACOB
> Why – why would I have to
> wear something like this?

> NEWT
> Because your skull is
> susceptible to breakage under
> immense force.

NEWT *runs on. Utterly terrified,* JACOB *puts on the hat and chases after* NEWT.

SCENE 52
EXT. GOLDSTEIN RESIDENCE—NIGHT

TINA *and* QUEENIE *lean out of their bedroom window,
craning into the dark. Another bellowing roar reverberates
through the winter night. Other windows open, neighbours
stare sleepily over the city.*

SCENE 53
INT. GOLDSTEIN RESIDENCE—NIGHT

TINA *and* QUEENIE *burst into the bedroom where*
JACOB *and* NEWT *are meant to be asleep. Every trace of
the two men has gone. Furious,* TINA *storms off to dress.*
QUEENIE *looks upset.*

> QUEENIE
> But we made 'em cocoa ...

SCENE 54
EXT. CENTRAL PARK ZOO—NIGHT

NEWT *and* JACOB *run up to the now half-empty zoo, the outer walls of which have been demolished in places. A large pile of rubble lies at the entrance.*

Another bellowing roar echoes around the brick building. NEWT *produces a body protector.*

> NEWT
> Okay, if you just, uh, pop this
> on.

NEWT *stands behind* JACOB, *fastening the breastplate over him.*

> JACOB
>
> Okay.

> NEWT
>
> Now there's absolutely nothing for you to worry about.

> JACOB
>
> Tell me – has anyone ever believed you when you told them not to worry?

> NEWT
>
> My philosophy is that worrying means you suffer twice.

JACOB *digests* NEWT'S *'wisdom'.*

NEWT *picks up his case and* JACOB *follows him, stumbling over rubble and debris.*

They stand at the entrance to the zoo. A loud snort comes from within.

> NEWT
> She's in season. She needs to
> mate.

*ANGLE ON the Erumpent – a large, rotund, rhino-like
creature with a massive horn protruding from her forehead.
Five times his size, she is nuzzling up against the enclosure
of a terrified hippo.*

NEWT *takes out a tiny vial of liquid – he pulls the stopper
out with his teeth and spits it to the side before dabbing a
spot of the liquid onto each wrist.* JACOB *looks at him – the
smell is pungent.*

> NEWT
> Erumpent musk – she is mad
> for it.

NEWT *passes* JACOB *the open bottle and heads into the
zoo.*

TIME CUT:

NEWT *places his case down on the ground near the
Erumpent and slowly, seductively, opens it.*

*He begins to perform a 'mating ritual' – a series of
grunts, wiggles, rolls and groans – to gain the Erumpent's
attention.*

Finally the Erumpent turns away from the hippo – she is interested in NEWT. *They face each other, circle round, undulating weirdly. The Erumpent's demeanour is puppy-like, her horn glowing orange.*

NEWT *rolls along the floor – the Erumpent copies, moving nearer and nearer to the open case.*

> NEWT
> Good girl – come on – into
> the case ...

JACOB *takes a sniff of the Erumpent musk. As he does so, a fish flies through the air and jolts him, spilling the musk.*

The wind changes. Trees rustle. The Erumpent takes a deep breath in – she can smell the new, more powerful aroma coming from JACOB.

JACOB *looks around. A seal sits behind him looking guilty, before cheekily running away.*

When JACOB *turns back, he sees the Erumpent is now on her feet, staring at him.*

ANGLE ON NEWT *and* JACOB, *realising what is about to happen.*

BACK TO SCENE:

The Erumpent charges towards the source of the smell,
bellowing madly. JACOB *wails, running as fast as he can*
in the opposite direction. The Erumpent gives chase – they
crash through rubble and ice-ponds, before charging across
the snow-covered park.

NEWT *draws his wand—*

NEWT

> *Repar—*

Before he can finish, his wand is whipped out of his hand
by a baboon, which runs off, clutching its prize.

NEWT

Merlin's beard!

ANGLE ON JACOB, *tanking along, the Erumpent close*
behind him.

ANGLE ON NEWT, *face to face with the curious baboon,*
which examines his wand.

NEWT *breaks a bit of twig from a branch and holds it out,*
trying to persuade the baboon to trade with him.

NEWT

They're exactly the same ...
same thing.

BACK TO JACOB:

In trying to climb a tree, JACOB *has ended up hanging precariously upside down from a branch.*

> JACOB
> *(bellowing, terrified)*
> Newt!

We see the Erumpent below him. She lies on her back, wiggling her legs in the air invitingly.

ANGLE BACK ON NEWT – *the baboon shakes* NEWT'S *wand.*

> NEWT
> No, no, no, don't!

NEWT *looks worried – BANG – the wand 'goes off', the spell knocking the baboon backwards. The wand flies back to* NEWT.

> NEWT
> I'm so sorry—

ANGLE ON JACOB – *the Erumpent is now on her feet. She charges towards the tree, digging her horn deep into the trunk. The tree bubbles with glowing liquid before exploding and crashing to the ground.*

JACOB *is thrown off, rolling down a steep, snowy hill and onto the frozen lake below.*

The Erumpent charges after him, hits the ice and skids. NEWT *comes careering down the hill, also hitting the ice. He performs an athletic slide, his case open – the Erumpent is mere feet from* JACOB *when the case swallows her.*

NEWT
Good show, Mr Kowalski!

JACOB *holds out his hand to shake.*

JACOB
Call me Jacob.

They shake hands.

THIRD PERSON POV: Someone watches as NEWT *hauls* JACOB *up and they slip and slide across the frozen lake as fast as they can.*

NEWT
Well, two down, one to go.

HOLD ON TINA *as she hides on the bridge above them, peeking down.*

NEWT (*O.S.*)
(*to* JACOB*)*
In you hop.

We see the case sitting alone below the bridge.

TINA *quickly appears around the corner and hurriedly sits on the case. She closes the catches, looking shocked but determined.*

> ANNOUNCER (*V.O.*)
> Ladies and gentlemen ...

SCENE 55
INT. CITY HALL—NIGHT

A large ornately decorated hall, covered in patriotic emblems. Hundreds of glamorously dressed people sit at round tables, looking towards a stage at the far end. Over this stage hangs a large poster of SENATOR SHAW *with a slogan reading 'America's Future'.*

An ANNOUNCER *stands behind the microphone.*

> ANNOUNCER
> ... now tonight's keynote
> speaker needs no
> introduction from me. He's
> been mentioned as a future

President – and if you don't
believe me, just read his
daddy's newspapers—

Indulgent laughter from the crowd. We see SHAW SR *and*
LANGDON *seated at a table, surrounded by the crème de
la crème of New York society.*

ANNOUNCER
—ladies and gentlemen, I
give you the Senator for New
York, Henry Shaw!

Tumultuous applause. SENATOR SHAW *bounds forwards,
acknowledging the cheers, pointing and winking at
intimates in the crowd, and mounts the steps.*

SCENE 56
EXT. DARK STREET—NIGHT

*Something is streaking through the streets, too large
and fast for a human. Strange, laboured breathing and
snarling – it is inhuman, beast-like.*

SCENE 57
EXT. STREET NEAR CITY HALL—NIGHT

TINA *is hurrying along, clutching the case. Street lights start going out around her. She stops, feels something pass in the darkness – turns, staring, scared.*

SCENE 58
INT. CITY HALL—NIGHT

> SENATOR SHAW
> ... and it's true we have made
> some progress, but there is no
> reward for idleness. So just as
> the odious saloons have been
> banished ...

A strange, haunting noise comes from the organ pipes at the back of the room. Everyone turns to look, the SENATOR *pauses.*

SENATOR SHAW
... so now the pool halls, and
these private parlours ...

The strange noise gets louder.

Guests turn to look again. The SENATOR *seems anxious.
People mutter.*

*Suddenly something explodes forth from underneath the
organ. Something huge and bestial, although invisible, is
soaring down the hall – tables fly, people are thrown, lights
smash and people scream as it carves a line towards the stage.*

SENATOR SHAW *is thrown backwards against his own
poster, raised up high and suspended for a moment in mid-
air before being brought down with a violent crash – dead.*

*The 'beast' rips at his poster – a frenzied slashing with
harsh, noisy breathing – before swarming back out from
where it came.*

Sounds of anguish and panic from the crowd as SHAW
SR *fights through the debris towards his son's torn and
bleeding body.*

ANGLE ON SENATOR SHAW'S *body, his face brutally
scarred.* SHAW SR *looks devastated as he crouches beside his
son.*

ANGLE ON LANGDON, *now on his feet, slightly drunk.*
Determined, perhaps triumphant.

LANGDON

WITCHES!

SCENE 59
INT. MACUSA LOBBY—NIGHT

*Focus on the gigantic dial showing the MAGICAL
EXPOSURE THREAT LEVEL. The hand moves from
SEVERE to EMERGENCY.*

TINA, *case in hand, runs up the lobby steps, past witches
and wizards huddled in groups, whispering nervously.*

HEINRICH EBERSTADT (*V.O.*)
Our American friends have
permitted a breach of the
Statute of Secrecy ...

SCENE 60
INT. PENTAGRAM OFFICE—NIGHT

An impressive hall arranged like an old parliament
debating chamber. Every seat is occupied by wizards from
all parts of the world. MADAM PICQUERY *is presiding,*
GRAVES *at her side.*

The Swiss delegate is speaking.

HEINRICH EBERSTADT
... that threatens to expose
us all.

MADAM PICQUERY
I will not be lectured by
the man who let Gellert
Grindelwald slip through his
fingers—

A hologram image of SENATOR SHAW'S *dead and twisted body floats high above the room, emitting a glowing light.*

All heads turn as TINA *hurries into the chamber.*

> TINA
> Madam President, I'm so
> sorry to interrupt, but this is
> critical—

Echoing silence. TINA *slides to a halt in the middle of the marble floor before realising exactly what she's walked into. The delegates stare at her.*

> MADAM PICQUERY
> You'd better have an excellent
> excuse for this intrusion,
> Miss Goldstein.

> TINA
> Yes – I do.
> *(stepping forwards*
> *to address her)*
> Ma'am. Yesterday a
> wizard entered New York
> with a case. This case of
> magical creatures, and –
> unfortunately – some have
> escaped.

MADAM PICQUERY
He arrived yesterday? You
have known for twenty-four
hours that an unregistered
wizard set magical beasts
loose in New York and you
see fit to tell us only when a
man has been killed?

TINA
Who has been killed?

MADAM PICQUERY
Where is this man?

TINA *sets the case flat on the floor and thumps the lid.*
After a second or two, it creaks open. First NEWT, *then*
JACOB *emerge, looking sheepish and nervous.*

BRITISH ENVOY
Scamander?

NEWT
(closing the case)
Oh – er – hello, Minister.

MOMOLU WOTORSON
Theseus Scamander? The war
hero?

BRITISH ENVOY
No, this is his little brother.
And what in the name of
Merlin are you doing in New
York?

NEWT
I came to buy an Appaloosa
Puffskein, sir.

BRITISH ENVOY
(*suspicious*)
Right. What are you really
doing here?

MADAM PICQUERY
(*to* TINA, *about* JACOB)
Goldstein – and who is this?

TINA
This is Jacob Kowalski,
Madam President, he's a No-
Maj who got bitten by one of
Mr Scamander's creatures.

*Furious reaction from the MACUSA employees and
dignitaries all around.*

MINISTERS
(whispers)
No-Maj? Obliviated?

NEWT *is absorbed in the image of* SENATOR SHAW'S
body floating around the room.

NEWT
Merlin's beard!

MADAM YA ZHOU
You know which of your
creatures was responsible, Mr
Scamander?

NEWT
No creature did this ... don't
pretend! You must know
what that was, look at the
marks ...

ANGLE ON SENATOR SHAW'S *face.*

ANGLE ON NEWT.

NEWT
That was an Obscurus.

Mass consternation, muttering, exclamations. GRAVES *looks
alert.*

MADAM PICQUERY
You go too far, Mr Scamander.
There is no Obscurial in
America. Impound that case,
Graves!

GRAVES *summons the case; it lands next to him.* NEWT
draws his wand.

NEWT
(*to* GRAVES)
No … give that b—!

MADAM PICQUERY
Arrest them!

A dazzling eruption of spells hit NEWT, TINA *and* JACOB,
all of whom are slammed to their knees. NEWT'S *wand
flies out of his hand, caught by* GRAVES.

GRAVES *stands and picks up the case.*

NEWT
(*magically restrained*)
No – no – don't hurt those
creatures – please, you don't
understand – nothing in
there is dangerous, nothing!

> MADAM PICQUERY
> We'll be the judges of that!
> *(to the Aurors now*
> *standing behind them)*
> Take them to the cells!

ANGLE ON GRAVES *watching* TINA *as she,* NEWT *and*
JACOB *are dragged away.*

> NEWT
> *(screaming, desperate)*
> Don't hurt those creatures –
> there is nothing in there that
> is dangerous. Please don't
> hurt my creatures – they are
> not dangerous ... please, they
> are not dangerous!

SCENE 61
INT. MACUSA CELL—DAY

NEWT, TINA *and* JACOB *sitting,* NEWT *with his head in*
his hands, still in utter despair about his creatures. Finally
TINA, *on the verge of tears, breaks the silence.*

TINA

I am so sorry about your
creatures, Mr Scamander. I
truly am.

NEWT *remains silent.*

JACOB
(*sotto voce, to* TINA)
Can someone please tell
me what this Obscurial
Obscurius thing is? Please?

TINA
(*also sotto voce*)
There hasn't been one for
centuries—

NEWT

I met one in Sudan three
months ago. There used to
be more of them but they
still exist. Before wizards
went underground, when
we were still being hunted
by Muggles, young wizards
and witches sometimes
tried to suppress their
magic to avoid persecution.
Instead of learning to

harness or to control their
powers, they developed
what was called an
Obscurus.

TINA
(*off* JACOB'S *confusion*)
It's an unstable,
uncontrollable dark force that
busts out and – and attacks ...
and then vanishes ...

*As she talks, we see the penny dropping. An Obscurus fits
everything she knows about the perpetrator of the New
York attacks.*

TINA
(*to* NEWT)
Obscurials can't survive long,
can they?

NEWT
There's no documented case
of any Obscurial surviving
past the age of ten. The one I
met in Africa was eight when
she – she was eight when she
died.

JACOB
What are you telling me
here – that Senator Shaw was
killed by a – by a *kid*?

NEWT'S *look says 'yes'.*

SCENE 62
INT. SECOND SALEM CHURCH, MAIN HALL— DAY— MONTAGE

MODESTY *approaches the long table at which many orphan children sit hungrily eating.*

> MODESTY
> (*continuing her chant*)
> … my momma, your momma,
> flying on a switch,
> My momma, your momma,
> witches never cry,

My momma, your momma,
witches gonna die!

MODESTY *gathers several of the children's leaflets from the table.*

> MODESTY
> Witch number one, drown in
> a river!
> Witch number two, gotta
> noose to give her!
> Witch number three ...

TIME CUT:

The children, having finished their meal, leave the table with their leaflets and head for the door.

> CHASTITY
> *(calling after them)*
> Hand out your leaflets! I'll
> know if you dump 'em.
> Tell me if you see anything
> suspicious.

CLOSE ON CREDENCE *– he's washing dishes, but watching the children intently.*

MODESTY *follows the last of the children out of the church.*

SCENE 63
EXT. STREET OUTSIDE SECOND SALEM
CHURCH—DAY

MODESTY *stands in the middle of the busy street. She throws her leaflets high into the air, watching with glee as they fall around her.*

SCENE 64
INT. MACUSA CELL/CORRIDOR—DAY

Two EXECUTIONERS *in white coats lead a shackled* NEWT *and* TINA *down to a dark basement, away from the cell.*

NEWT *turns to look back.*

> NEWT
> *(over his shoulder)*
> It was good to make your
> acquaintance, Jacob, and I
> hope you get your bakery.

ANGLE ON JACOB, *scared, left behind, clutching at the bars of the cell. He waves forlornly after* NEWT.

SCENE 65
INT. INTERROGATION ROOM—DAY

A small, bare room, black-walled and windowless.

GRAVES *sits opposite* NEWT *at an interrogation desk, a file open in front of him.* NEWT *squints forward, a bright light shining into his eyes.*

TINA *stands behind, flanked by the two* EXECUTIONERS.

> GRAVES
> You're an interesting man,
> Mr Scamander.

> TINA
> *(stepping forwards)*
> Mr Graves—

GRAVES *holds a finger to his lips, signalling for* TINA *to be silent. The gesture is patronising, but authoritative.* TINA *looks kowtowed – she obeys, stepping back into the shadows.*

GRAVES *examines the file on his desk.*

> GRAVES
> You were thrown out of
> Hogwarts for endangering
> human life—

> NEWT
> That was an accident!

> GRAVES
> —with a beast. Yet one of
> your teachers argued strongly
> against your expulsion.
> Now, what makes Albus
> Dumbledore so fond of you?

> NEWT
> I really couldn't say.

> GRAVES
> So setting a pack of
> dangerous creatures loose
> here was just another
> accident, is that right?

> NEWT
> Why would I do it
> deliberately?

GRAVES

To expose wizardkind. To
provoke war between the
magical and non-magical
worlds.

NEWT

Mass slaughter for the greater
good, you mean?

GRAVES

Yes. Quite.

NEWT

I'm not one of Grindelwald's
fanatics, Mr Graves.

A tiny change of expression tells us that NEWT *has scored
a hit.* GRAVES *is looking more menacing.*

GRAVES

I wonder what you can
tell me about this, Mr
Scamander?

With a slow move of his hand, GRAVES *raises up the
Obscurus from* NEWT'S *case. He brings it onto the desk –
it is pulsing, swirling and hissing.*

CLOSE ON TINA *as she stares, disbelieving.*

GRAVES *reaches a hand towards the Obscurus – he's utterly fascinated. At his sudden close proximity, the Obscurus swirls faster, bubbling and shrinking backwards.*

NEWT *turns instinctively to* TINA. *Without fully realising why, it is she whom he wants to convince.*

> NEWT
> It's an Obscurus—
> (*off her look*)
> But, it's not what you think. I
> managed to separate it from
> the Sudanese girl as I tried to
> save her – I wanted to take it
> home, to study it—
> (*off* TINA'S *shock*)
> But it cannot survive outside
> that box, it could not hurt
> anyone, Tina!

> GRAVES
> So it's useless without the
> host?

> NEWT
> 'Useless? Useless?' That is a
> parasitical magical force that
> killed a child. What on earth
> would you use it for?

NEWT, *anger finally boiling within him, stares at* GRAVES. TINA, *reacting to the atmosphere, also looks to* GRAVES – *concern and trepidation written across her face.*

GRAVES *stands, brushing off the questions, turning the blame back onto* NEWT.

> GRAVES
> You fool nobody, Mr Scamander. You brought this Obscurus into the city of New York in the hope of causing mass disruption, breaking the Statute of Secrecy and revealing the magical world—

> NEWT
> You know that can't hurt anyone, you know that!

> GRAVES
> —you are therefore guilty of a treasonous betrayal of your fellow wizards and are sentenced to death. Miss Goldstein, who has aided and abetted you—

> NEWT
> No, she's done nothing of the
> kind—

> GRAVES
> —she receives the same
> sentence.

The two EXECUTIONERS *step forwards. They calmly, intrusively, press the tips of their wands into* NEWT *and* TINA'S *necks.*

TINA *is so overcome with shock and fear that she can barely speak.*

> GRAVES
> *(to the* EXECUTIONERS*)*
> Just do it immediately. I will
> inform President Picquery
> myself.

> NEWT
> Tina.

GRAVES *again places a finger to his lips.*

> GRAVES
> Shhhh.
> *(waving to the*
> EXECUTIONERS*)*
> Please.

SCENE 66
INT. SHABBY BASEMENT MEETING ROOM—DAY

QUEENIE *is carrying a tray of coffee and mugs towards a meeting room.*

Suddenly she freezes, her eyes widen, a look of terror across her face. She drops the tray – cups smashing on the floor.

An assortment of low-level MACUSA functionaries turn to stare at her. QUEENIE *stares back, stunned, before running away down the corridor.*

SCENE 67
INT. CORRIDOR LEADING TO DEATH CELL—DAY

A long black metallic corridor leads into a pure white cell, which consists of a chair suspended magically over a square pool of rippling potion.

NEWT *and* TINA *are forced into this room by the*
EXECUTIONERS. *A guard stands at the door.*

> TINA
> (*to* EXECUTIONER 1)
> Don't do this – Bernadette –
> please—

> EXECUTIONER 1
> It don't hurt.

TINA *is led to the edge of the pool. She begins panicking,*
her breathing heavy and erratic.

The smiling EXECUTIONER 1 *raises a wand and carefully*
extracts TINA'S *happy memories from her head.* TINA
instantly calms – her expression now vacant, other-worldly.

EXECUTIONER 1 *casts the memories into the potion,*
which ripples, coming alive with scenes from TINA'S *life.*

A young TINA *smiles up as her mother calls.*

> TINA'S MOTHER (*V.O.*)
> Tina … Tina … come on,
> pumpkin – time for bed. Are
> you ready?

> TINA
> Momma …

TINA'S MOTHER *appears in the pool, her expression loving and warm. The real* TINA *watches, smiling down.*

> EXECUTIONER 1
> Don't that look good. You
> wanna get in? Huh?

TINA *nods vacantly.*

SCENE 68
INT. MACUSA LOBBY—DAY

QUEENIE *stands in the crowded lobby. The elevator doors sound.*

ANGLE ON the elevator doors, which open revealing JACOB, *escorted by* SAM, *the Obliviator.*

QUEENIE *hurries towards them, determined.*

> QUEENIE
> Hey, Sam!

> SAM
> Hey, Queenie.

> QUEENIE
> They need you downstairs.
> I'll Obliviate this guy.

> SAM
> You ain't qualified.

Grim-faced, QUEENIE *reads his mind.*

> QUEENIE
> Hey, Sam – does Cecily know
> you been seeing Ruby?

ANGLE ON RUBY, *a MACUSA witch, standing ahead of them. She smiles at* SAM.

ANGLE ON QUEENIE *and* SAM *–* SAM *looks nervous.*

> SAM
> *(appalled)*
> How'd you—?

> QUEENIE
> Let me Obliviate this guy
> and she'll never hear about it
> from me.

Stunned, SAM *backs away.* QUEENIE *seizes* JACOB'S *arm and marches him off across the cavernous lobby.*

JACOB
What are you doin'?

QUEENIE
Shhhh! Teen's in trouble, I'm
trying to listen—
(she reads TINA'S mind)
Jacob, where's Newt's case?

JACOB
I think that guy Graves took
it—

QUEENIE
Okay, come on—

JACOB
What? You're not gonna
Obliviate me?

QUEENIE
Of course not – you're one of
us now!

QUEENIE hurries him towards the main staircase.

<u>SCENE 69</u>
INT. DEATH CELL—DAY

TINA *sits in the execution chair. She gazes down: beneath her swirl happy images of her family, her parents, a young* QUEENIE.

MEMORY:

We move into the pool and follow one of TINA'S *memories:* TINA *walks inside the Second Salem Church and up the stairs. She finds* MARY LOU, *standing over* CREDENCE, *belt in hand –* CREDENCE *looks terrified. In anger,* TINA *casts a spell, striking* MARY LOU. TINA *moves forward to comfort* CREDENCE.

TINA

It's okay.

ANGLE BACK ON real TINA, *still gazing into the pool, smiling wistfully.*

ANGLE ON NEWT, *who glances quickly down his own arm –* PICKETT *is clambering, quiet and agile, towards the shackles holding* NEWT'S *hands.*

SCENE 70
INT. CORRIDOR LEADING TO GRAVES'S OFFICE—DAY

ANGLE ON the door to GRAVES'S *office.*

> QUEENIE (O.S.)
> *Alohomora.*

We see QUEENIE *and* JACOB *standing awkwardly outside* GRAVES'S *office,* QUEENIE *trying desperately to open the door.*

> QUEENIE
> *Aberto ...*

The door remains locked.

> QUEENIE
> *(frustrated)*
> Ugh. He would know a fancy spell to lock his office.

SCENE 71
INT. DEATH CELL—DAY

Back to PICKETT *as he finishes unlocking the shackles holding* NEWT'S *wrists, and quickly climbs onto* EXECUTIONER 2'S *coat.*

> EXECUTIONER 2
> (*to* NEWT)
> Okay, let's get the good stuff
> out of you—

EXECUTIONER 2 *raises her wand to* NEWT'S *forehead.* NEWT *seizes his opportunity – he jumps backwards out of the way before revealing the Swooping Evil, which he throws forwards towards the pool. He then swiftly turns and punches the guard, knocking him out cold.*

The Swooping Evil has now expanded into a gigantic, spooky but weirdly beautiful butterfly-esque reptile with skeletal wings. It continues to circle round and round the pool.

PICKETT *clambers onto* EXECUTIONER 2'S *arm and bites, startling and distracting her, giving* NEWT *time to grab her arms and take aim with her wand. A spell fires, hitting* EXECUTIONER 1, *who drops to the floor, her wand falling into the pool. As it falls, the liquid rises up in viscous black bubbles, instantly engulfing the wand.*

In reaction, TINA'S *memories turn from good to bad: we see* MARY LOU, *pointing aggressively at* TINA.

> MARY LOU
>
> Witch!

TINA, *still enraptured by the pool, looks increasingly terrified. Her chair is lowering closer and closer to the liquid.*

The Swooping Evil glides across the room, knocking EXECUTIONER 2 *to the ground.*

SCENE 72
INT. CORRIDOR LEADING TO GRAVES'S OFFICE—DAY

After a quick glance around, JACOB *gives the door a hefty kick. It breaks open.* JACOB *stands guard as* QUEENIE *runs in and grabs* NEWT'S *case and* TINA'S *wand.*

<u>SCENE 73</u>
INT. DEATH CELL—DAY

TINA *snaps out of her reverie and screams.*

> TINA
> MR SCAMANDER!

The liquid has now turned into a black bubbling death potion. It rises up, surrounding TINA *on her chair.* TINA *stands up to get away, almost falling off in her haste. She tries desperately to regain her balance.*

> NEWT
> DON'T PANIC!

> TINA
> WHAT DO YOU SUGGEST
> I DO INSTEAD?

NEWT *makes a strange tutting sound, commanding the Swooping Evil to circle the pool once more.*

> NEWT
> Jump …

TINA *looks at the Swooping Evil – fearful, disbelieving.*

> TINA
> ARE YOU CRAZY?

NEWT

Jump on him.

NEWT *stands on the edge of the pool watching the Swooping Evil as it circles round and round* TINA.

NEWT

Tina, listen to me. I'll catch
you. Tina!

The two make intense eye contact, NEWT *trying to reassure …*

The liquid has now risen up in waves to TINA'S *full height – she's losing sight of* NEWT.

NEWT
(*insistent, very calm*)
I'll catch you. I've got you
Tina …

Suddenly NEWT *cries out.*

NEWT

Go!

TINA *jumps in between two of the waves, just as the Swooping Evil passes. She lands on its back, only inches away from the swirling liquid, then hops quickly forwards, straight into* NEWT'S *open arms.*

For a split second NEWT *and* TINA *gaze at each other, before* NEWT *raises his hand, recalling the Swooping Evil, which folds into a cocoon once more.*

NEWT *grabs* TINA'S *hand and heads for the exit.*

NEWT

Come on!

SCENE 74
INT. DEATH CELL CORRIDOR—DAY

QUEENIE *and* JACOB *march along the corridor with purpose.*

An alarm goes off in the distance – other wizards hurry past them in the opposite direction.

SCENE 75
INT. MACUSA LOBBY—MINUTES LATER—DAY

The alarm blares out across the lobby.

Confusion reigns among the crowd – people gather in groups, nervously chattering, others scurry about, urgent, anxious.

A team of Aurors hurtles across the lobby, headed directly for the stairs leading down to the basement.

SCENE 76
INT. DEATH CELL CORRIDOR/BASEMENT CORRIDOR—DAY

NEWT *and* TINA, *hand in hand, charge through the basement corridors. Suddenly accosted by the group of Aurors, they turn, darting behind pillars, just missing the fired curses and spells.*

NEWT *again sends out the Swooping Evil, which swirls overhead, flying in and out of pillars, blocking curses and knocking Aurors to the ground.*

ANGLE ON the Swooping Evil using its proboscis to probe in one of the Auror's ears.

> NEWT
> (*making a clicking sound*)
> LEAVE HIS BRAINS. Come
> on! Come on!

TINA and NEWT *run onwards, the Swooping Evil flying after, blocking curses as it goes.*

> TINA
> What *is* that thing?

> NEWT
> Swooping Evil.

> TINA
> Well, I love it!

ANGLE ON QUEENIE *and* JACOB, *walking briskly through the basement.* NEWT *and* TINA *sprint round the corner and almost collide with them. The four stare at one another, panic on all their faces.*

Finally QUEENIE *gestures to the case.*

> QUEENIE
> Get in!

SCENE 77
INT. STAIRS LEADING TO CELLS—MOMENTS
LATER—DAY

GRAVES *moves down the stairs with urgency. For the first time, a look of panic on his face.*

SCENE 78
INT. MACUSA LOBBY—MINUTES LATER—DAY

QUEENIE *moves quickly across the lobby floor, trying desperately not to be conspicuous in her haste, but acutely aware of the need to leave. A flustered* ABERNATHY *emerges from a crowd of wizards.*

> ABERNATHY
> Queenie!

QUEENIE, *poised at the top of the stairs, turns and composes herself.* ABERNATHY *moves towards her, straightening his tie, trying to appear calm and authoritative –* QUEENIE *obviously makes him nervous.*

ABERNATHY
(*a large smile*)
Where you going?

QUEENIE *puts on an alluringly innocent expression and holds the case behind her back.*

QUEENIE
I'm ... I'm sick, Mr
Abernathy.

She coughs a little, widening her eyes.

ABERNATHY
Again? Well – what've you
got there?

A beat.

QUEENIE *thinks fast, her face quickly breaking into a breathtaking smile.*

QUEENIE
Ladies' things.

QUEENIE *produces the case and innocently trots up the steps towards* ABERNATHY.

QUEENIE
You wanna take a look? I
don't mind.

ABERNATHY *is overcome with embarrassment.*

> ABERNATHY
> *(swallowing hard)*
> Oh! Good gravy, no! I – you
> get well now!

> QUEENIE
> *(smiling sweetly and
> arranging his tie)*
> Thanks!

QUEENIE *immediately turns and hurries down the stairs
leaving* ABERNATHY *– heart racing – staring after her.*

SCENE 79
EXT. STREETS OF NEW YORK—LATE AFTERNOON

HIGH WIDE above New York. We zoom over rooftops before diving down through streets and alleyways, past speeding cars and cackling children.

We come to rest in an alleyway at the Second Salem Church, where CREDENCE *is pasting up posters advertising* MARY LOU'S *next meeting.*

GRAVES *Apparates in the alleyway.* CREDENCE, *startled, backs away, but* GRAVES *makes straight for him, his tone and manner urgent, forceful.*

GRAVES
Credence. Have you found
the child?

CREDENCE
I can't.

GRAVES, *impatient but feigning calm, holds out his*
hand – suddenly seeming caring, affectionate.

GRAVES
Show me.

CREDENCE *whimpers and cowers, almost backing further*
away. GRAVES *gently takes* CREDENCE'S *hand in his*
own and examines it – the hand is covered in deep red cuts,
sore and bleeding.

GRAVES
Shhhh. My boy, the sooner
we find this child, the sooner
you can put that pain in the
past where it belongs.

GRAVES *gently, almost seductively, moves his thumb*
across the cuts, healing them instantly. CREDENCE *stares.*

GRAVES *seems to make a decision. He puts on an earnest,*
trustworthy expression as, from his pocket, he produces a
chain bearing the symbol of the Deathly Hallows.

GRAVES
I want you to have this,
Credence. I would trust very
few with it—

GRAVES *moves close, placing the chain around*
CREDENCE'S *neck as he whispers.*

GRAVES
Very few.

GRAVES *places his hands on either side of* CREDENCE'S
neck, drawing him in, his speech quiet, intimate.

GRAVES
… but you – you're different.

CREDENCE *is unsure, both nervous of and attracted by*
GRAVES'S *behaviour.*

GRAVES *rests his hand on* CREDENCE'S *heart, covering*
the pendant.

GRAVES
Now, when you find the
child, touch this symbol and
I will know, and I will come
to you.

GRAVES *moves even closer to* CREDENCE, *his face*

inches from the boy's neck – the effect is both alluring and threatening – as he whispers.

> GRAVES
> Do this and you will be
> honoured among wizards.
> For ever.

GRAVES *pulls* CREDENCE *into a hug which, with his hand on* CREDENCE'S *neck, seems more controlling than affectionate.* CREDENCE, *overwhelmed by the seeming affection, closes his eyes and relaxes slightly.*

GRAVES *slowly backs away, stroking* CREDENCE'S *neck.* CREDENCE *keeps his eyes closed, longing for the human contact to continue.*

> GRAVES
> *(whispers)*
> The child is dying, Credence.
> Time is running out.

Abruptly, GRAVES *strides back down the alleyway and Disapparates.*

SCENE 80
EXT. ROOFTOP WITH PIGEON COOP—DUSK

A rooftop overlooking the whole city. In the middle sits a small wooden shed, which houses a pigeon coop.

NEWT *steps up onto a ledge and stands looking over the immense city.* PICKETT *sits on his shoulder, clicking.*

JACOB *is inside the shed, looking at the pigeon coop as* QUEENIE *enters.*

> QUEENIE
> Your grandfather kept
> pigeons? Mine bred owls. I
> used to love feeding 'em.

ANGLE ON NEWT *and* TINA – TINA *has joined* NEWT *in standing on the ledge.*

> TINA
> Graves always insisted the
> disturbances were caused by
> a beast. We need to catch all
> your creatures, so he can't keep
> using them as a scapegoat.

> NEWT
> There's only one still missing.
> Dougal, my Demiguise.

> TINA

Dougal?

> NEWT

Slight problem is that ... um,
he's invisible.

> TINA
> *(this is so ridiculous that*
> *she can't help but smile)*

Invisible?

> NEWT

Yes – most of the time ... he
does ... um ...

> TINA

How do you catch something
that—

> NEWT
> *(beginning to smile)*

With immense difficulty.

> TINA

Oh ...

They smile at each other – there's a new warmth between
them, NEWT *still awkward but somehow unable to stop*
staring at TINA *as she smiles.*

TINA *moves slowly towards* NEWT.

A beat.

>   TINA
> Gnarlak!

>   NEWT
>   *(taken aback)*
> Excuse me?

>   TINA
>   *(conspiratorial, excited)*
> Gnarlak – he was an
> informant of mine when I
> was an Auror! He used to
> trade in magical creatures on
> the side—

>   NEWT
> He wouldn't happen to have
> an interest in paw prints
> would he?

>   TINA
> He's interested in anything he
> can sell.

SCENE 81
EXT. THE BLIND PIG—NIGHT

TINA *leads the group down an insalubrious back alley covered in bins, crates and discarded objects. She locates a set of steps leading to a basement apartment and motions them down.*

The steps appear to lead to a dead end: the doorway has been bricked up. Instead, a poster of a simpering debutante in evening dress, gazing at herself in a mirror, covers the end of the walkway.

TINA *and* QUEENIE *stand in front of this poster. They turn to each other and, in unison, raise their wands. As they do so, their work clothes transform into stunning flapper party dresses.* TINA *looks up at* NEWT, *somewhat embarrassed by her new attire.* QUEENIE *gazes at* JACOB, *a cheeky smile on her face.*

TINA *steps towards the poster and slowly raises her hand. As she does so, the eyes of the debutante move upwards, following her every move.* TINA *knocks slowly on the door four times.*

NEWT, *sensing the need for a change, hastily magics himself a small bow tie.* JACOB *looks on, jealously.*

A hatch opens: the painted eyes of the debutante whip back to reveal the gaze of a suspicious guard.

SCENE 82
INT. THE BLIND PIG—NIGHT

A seedy, low-ceilinged speakeasy for the down and out of New York's magical community. Every witch and wizard criminal in New York is here, their wanted posters hanging proudly on the walls. A glimpse of 'GELLERT

*GRINDELWALD: WANTED FOR NO-MAJ SLAYINGS
IN EUROPE'.*

A glamorous goblin JAZZ SINGER *croons on a stage full of
goblin musicians, smoky images wafting from her wand to
illustrate her lyrics. All is dingy and shabby, an atmosphere
of menacing fun.*

> JAZZ SINGER
> The phoenix cried fat tears of
>   pearl,
> When the dragon snapped up
>   his best girl,
> And the Billywig forgot to
>   twirl,
> When his sweetheart left him
>   cold,
> And the unicorn done lost his
>   horn,
> And the Hippogriff feels all
>   forlorn,
> 'Cause their lady loves have
>   upped and gawn,
> Or that's what I've been
>   told—

JACOB *stands at the seemingly unmanned bar, waiting to
be served.*

> JACOB
> How do I get a drink in this
> joint?

Out of nowhere, a thin bottle of brown liquid zooms towards him. He catches it, stunned.

The head of a HOUSE-ELF *peers up at him from behind the bar.*

> HOUSE-ELF
> What? Ain't you ever seen a
> house-elf before?

> JACOB
> Oh, no, yeah, no, yeah of
> course I have ... I love house-
> elves.

JACOB *tries to act nonchalant – he removes the cork from the bottle.*

> JACOB
> My uncle's a house-elf.

The HOUSE-ELF *– not fooled – raises himself up, leaning on the bar to stare at* JACOB.

QUEENIE *approaches. She looks downcast as she orders.*

QUEENIE
Six shots of gigglewater and a
lobe blaster, please.

The HOUSE-ELF *reluctantly shuffles off to fulfil her request.* JACOB *and* QUEENIE *look at each other.* JACOB *reaches out and takes one of the gigglewater shots.*

QUEENIE
Are all No-Majs like you?

JACOB
(*trying to be serious,
almost seductive*)
No, I'm the only one like me.

Maintaining strong eye contact with QUEENIE, JACOB *knocks back the shot. Suddenly he emits a raucous, high-pitched giggle.* QUEENIE *laughs sweetly at his look of surprise.*

ANGLE ON a HOUSE-ELF *serving a drink to a giant, whose hand dwarfs the mug he is handed.*

ANGLE ON NEWT *and* TINA *sitting at a table alone. There's an awkward silence.* NEWT *studies the characters in the room: hooded and heavily scarred witches and wizards gamble magical artefacts in a game with runic dice.*

TINA
(*looking around*)
I've arrested half of the
people in here.

NEWT
You can tell me to mind my
own business ... but I saw
something in that death
potion back there. I saw
you – hugging – that Second
Salem boy.

TINA
His name's Credence. His
mother beats him. She beats
all those kids she adopted,
but she seems to hate him the
most.

NEWT
(*realising*)
And she was the No-Maj you
attacked?

TINA
That's how I lost my job.
I went for her in front of
a meeting of her crazy
followers – they all had to

be Obliviated. It was a big
scandal.

QUEENIE *signals from across the room.*

> QUEENIE
> *(whispers)*
> It's him.

GNARLAK *has emerged from the depths of the speakeasy.*
Smoking a cigar and smartly dressed, for a goblin, he has
a sly, smooth demeanour like a mafia boss. He eyes the
newcomers as he walks.

> JAZZ SINGER (O.S.)
> Yes, love has set the beasts astir,
> The dang'rous and the meek
> concur,
> It's ruffled feathers, fleece and
> fur,
> 'Cause love drives all of us
> wild.

GNARLAK *sits himself at the end of their table, an air of*
confidence and dangerous control. A HOUSE-ELF *hastily*
brings him a drink.

> GNARLAK
> So – you're the guy with the
> case full of monsters, huh?

> NEWT
>
> News travels fast. I was
> hoping you'd be able to tell
> me if there have been any
> sightings. Tracks. That sort of
> thing.

GNARLAK *downs his drink. Another* HOUSE-ELF *brings
him a document to sign.*

> GNARLAK
>
> You've got a big price on your
> head, Mr Scamander. Why
> should I help you instead of
> turnin' you in?

> NEWT
>
> I take it I'll have to make it
> worth your while?

The HOUSE-ELF *scurries off holding the signed
document.*

> GNARLAK
>
> Hmm – let's consider it a
> cover charge.

NEWT *pulls out a couple of Galleons and slides them
across the table towards* GNARLAK, *who barely looks up.*

> GNARLAK
> (*not impressed*)
> Huh – MACUSA's offerin'
> more'n that.

A beat.

NEWT *pulls out a beautiful metal instrument and places it
on the table.*

> GNARLAK
> Lunascope? I got five.

NEWT *rummages in his coat pocket and pulls out a
glowing, frozen ruby egg instead.*

> NEWT
> Frozen Ashwinder egg!

> GNARLAK
> (*finally interested*)
> You see – now we're—

GNARLAK *suddenly spots* PICKETT, *who is peeking out of*
NEWT'S *pocket.*

> GNARLAK
> —wait a minute – that's a
> Bowtruckle, right?

PICKETT *quickly retreats and* NEWT *puts a hand protectively over his pocket.*

> NEWT
>
> No.

> GNARLAK
>
> Ah, come on, that's a
> Bowtruckle – they pick
> locks – am I right?

> NEWT
>
> You're not having him.

> GNARLAK
>
> Well, good luck gettin' back
> alive, Mr Scamander, what
> with the whole of MACUSA
> on your back.

GNARLAK *gets up and walks away.*

> NEWT
> *(in agony)*
>
> All right.

GNARLAK, *turned away from* NEWT, *smiles viciously.*

NEWT *extracts* PICKETT *from his pocket.* PICKETT *clings to* NEWT'S *hands, madly clicking and whining.*

> NEWT

Pickett ...

NEWT *slowly hands* PICKETT *over to* GNARLAK.
PICKETT *reaches his little arms forward, imploring* NEWT
to take him back. NEWT *cannot look at him.*

> GNARLAK

Ah, yeah ...
> > (*to* NEWT)

Somethin' invisible's been
wreakin' havoc around Fifth
Avenue. You may wanna
check out Macy's department
store. Might help what you're
looking for.

> NEWT
> > (*sotto voce*)

Dougal ...
> > (*to* GNARLAK)

Right, one last thing. There's
a Mr Graves who works at
MACUSA – I was wondering
what you knew of his
background.

GNARLAK *stares. A sense that there is much that he could
say – and that he'd rather die than say it.*

GNARLAK
You ask too many questions,
Mr Scamander. That can get
you killed.

ANGLE ON a HOUSE-ELF *carrying a crate of bottles.*

HOUSE-ELF
MACUSA ARE COMING!

The HOUSE-ELF *Disapparates. Other customers
throughout the bar hurriedly do the same.*

TINA
(getting to her feet)
You tipped them off!

GNARLAK *stares at them, chuckling menacingly.*

Behind QUEENIE, *the wanted posters on the wall update to
show* NEWT *and* TINA'S *faces.*

Aurors begin Apparating into the speakeasy.

JACOB, *seemingly innocent, saunters up to* GNARLAK.

JACOB
Sorry, Mr Gnarlak—

JACOB *punches* GNARLAK *straight in the face, knocking him backwards.* QUEENIE *looks delighted.*

JACOB

– reminds me of my foreman!

Throughout the bar, various customers are being apprehended by the Aurors.

NEWT *scrambles about on the floor looking for* PICKETT. *Around him people are running, diving away from Aurors, trying to escape the bar.* NEWT *finally finds* PICKETT *on a table leg, grabs him and runs towards his group.*

JACOB *grabs another shot of gigglewater and knocks it back. He giggles uproariously as* NEWT *grabs his elbow and the group Disapparates.*

SCENE 83
INT. SECOND SALEM CHURCH—NIGHT

The long room is dimly lit by one set of lights. There's barely any noise.

CHASTITY *sits primly at the long table in the middle of the*

church. She formulaically arranges leaflets and places them
in little bags.

MODESTY *sits opposite in a nightdress, reading a book.
In the deep background,* MARY LOU *busies herself in her
bedroom.*

MODESTY *is the only one to register a small clunk from
upstairs.*

SCENE 84
INT. MODESTY'S BEDROOM—NIGHT

*A bleak room. A single bed, an oil-lamp, a sampler on the
wall: An Alphabet of Sin.* MODESTY'S *dolls lined up on a
shelf. One with a little noose around its neck, another tied
to a stake.*

CREDENCE *scrabbles to get underneath* MODESTY'S *bed.
He looks among the boxes and objects hidden there, then
suddenly stops, staring . . .*

SCENE 85
INT. SECOND SALEM CHURCH—NIGHT

MODESTY *stands at the bottom of the stairs, looking up.*
She slowly ascends.

SCENE 86
INT. MODESTY'S BEDROOM—NIGHT

ANGLE ON CREDENCE'S *face under the bed –*
CREDENCE *has found a toy wand. He stares, unable to*
draw his eyes from it.

Behind him, MODESTY *enters.*

> MODESTY
> Whatchoo doin', Credence?

CREDENCE *bangs his head on the bed in his haste to get out.*
He emerges, dusty and scared. He is relieved to see that it is
only MODESTY *but she, on seeing the wand, is terrified.*

> CREDENCE
> Where'd you get this?

> MODESTY
> *(frightened whisper)*
> Give it back, Credence. It's
> just a toy!

The door bangs open. MARY LOU *enters. Her gaze travels from* MODESTY *to* CREDENCE *and the toy wand – she is angrier than we have ever seen her.*

> MARY LOU
> *(to* CREDENCE*)*
> What is this?

SCENE 87
INT. SECOND SALEM CHURCH—NIGHT

HOLD ON CHASTITY, *still filling bags with leaflets.*

> MARY LOU (*O.S.*)
> Take it off!

CHASTITY *glances up towards the landing.*

SCENE 88
INT. SECOND SALEM CHURCH, UPSTAIRS
LANDING—NIGHT

MARY LOU *stands on the landing overlooking the main church below. Seen from below her figure is powerful, almost deified.*

MARY LOU *turns back towards* CREDENCE *and slowly, her face full of loathing, snaps the wand in two.*

As MODESTY *cowers,* CREDENCE *begins to remove his belt.* MARY LOU *holds out her hand and takes it.*

> CREDENCE
> (*pleading*)
> Ma . . .

> MARY LOU
> I am not your ma! Your
> mother was a wicked,
> unnatural woman!

MODESTY *forces her way between them.*

> MODESTY
> It was mine.

> MARY LOU
> Modesty—

Suddenly the belt is whipped out of MARY LOU'S *hands by supernatural means and falls like a dead snake in a far corner.* MARY LOU *looks at her hand – it is cut and bleeding from the force of the movement.*

MARY LOU *is stunned – she glances between* MODESTY *and* CREDENCE.

> MARY LOU
> (*frightened but
> covering it*)
> What is this?

MODESTY *stares defiantly directly back at her. In the background we see* CREDENCE *crouched down, hugging his knees and shaking.*

Trying to remain composed, MARY LOU *moves slowly to retrieve the belt. Before she can touch it, the belt slithers away across the floor.*

MARY LOU *backs away, tears of fear welling in her eyes. She turns slowly back towards the children.*

As she moves, an almighty force explodes into her: a bestial, screeching, dark mass that consumes her. Her scream is blood-curdling as the force throws her backwards, striking a wooden beam, flinging her over the balcony.

MARY LOU *smashes down onto the floor of the main church, her body lifeless, her face bearing the same scars seen on the face of* SENATOR SHAW.

The Dark force flies through the church, upending the table and destroying everything in sight.

SCENE 89
EXT. DEPARTMENT STORE—NIGHT

WIDE SHOT of a department store, its windows full of glamorously dressed mannequins.

JACOB approaches the shop windows staring at a handbag which, seemingly of its own accord, is sliding down the arm of a mannequin. NEWT, TINA and QUEENIE hurry up behind him and watch as the bag hovers in mid-air and floats off into the store.

SCENE 90
INT. DEPARTMENT STORE—NIGHT

A well-presented department store decorated for Christmas, with aisles full of expensive jewellery, shoes, hats and perfume. The place is shut down for the night, all the lights are off, no noises can be heard.

We see the handbag float down the central aisle, accompanied by small grunting noises.

NEWT *and the group quickly tiptoe through the store, coming to hide behind a large plastic Christmas display. They eye up the floating handbag.*

NEWT
(whispers)
So Demiguises are
fundamentally peaceful, but they
can give a nasty nip if provoked.

The Demiguise itself appears – a silvery-haired, orangutan-like creature, with a curious, wizened face – clambering over a display to reach a box of sweets.

NEWT
(to JACOB *and* QUEENIE*)*
You two ... head that way.

They start moving.

NEWT
And try very hard not to be
predictable.

JACOB *and* QUEENIE *exchange perplexed glances before heading off.*

A small roar can be heard in the distance.

ANGLE ON the Demiguise which, on hearing the sound, looks up towards the ceiling, before continuing to gather sweets, now shovelling them into its handbag.

TINA *(O.S.)*
Was that the Demiguise?

NEWT
No, I think it might be the reason
that the Demiguise is here.

ANGLE ON NEWT *and* TINA, *moving swiftly down an aisle towards the Demiguise, which is now moving away through the store.*

Realising it's been spotted, the Demiguise turns and looks at NEWT *quizzically, before moving up a set of side stairs.* NEWT *smiles and moves to follow.*

SCENE 91
INT. DEPARTMENT STORE, ATTIC
STOREROOM—NIGHT

A huge, dark attic-space, filled floor to ceiling with shelves packed with boxes of china: dinner services, teacups and general kitchenware.

The Demiguise walks along the attic in a patch of moonlight. It glances around before stopping and emptying its handbag full of confectionery.

> NEWT (*O.S.*)
> Its sight operates on
> probability, so it can foresee the
> most likely immediate future.

NEWT *comes into view, creeping up behind the Demiguise.*

> TINA (*O.S.*)
> So what's it doing now?

> NEWT
> It's babysitting.

The Demiguise holds up one of the sweets, seeming to offer it up to someone or something.

> TINA
> What did you just say—?

NEWT
(*calm and whispering*)
This is my fault. I thought
I had them all – but I must
have miscounted.

JACOB *and* QUEENIE *enter quietly.* NEWT *moves calmly
forwards and kneels beside the Demiguise, which makes
space for him in front of the sweets.* NEWT *carefully places
his case down.*

ANGLE ON TINA, *a shift of light reveals the scales of a
large creature hiding in the rafters of the attic.* TINA *looks
up in horror.*

TINA
It was babysitting that?

ANGLE ON *the ceiling as the face of an Occamy comes
into view – just like the small blue snake-like birds seen in
the case, this Occamy is huge, coiled round and round itself
to fill the entire attic roof-space.*

The Occamy moves slowly down towards NEWT *and the
Demiguise who, again, offers up a sweet.* NEWT *remains
very still.*

NEWT
Occamies are choranaptyxic.
So they – grow – to fill –
available – space.

The Occamy spots NEWT, *and cranes its head towards him.* NEWT *holds up a hand, gently.*

NEWT
Mummy's here.

ANGLE ON the Demiguise, whose eyes flash a brilliant blue – a sign that it's having a premonition.

FLASHCUTS:

A Christmas bauble rolls across the floor; the Occamy is panicking, NEWT *clasping its back, being flung about the room; the Demiguise is suddenly on* JACOB'S *back.*

BACK TO the Demiguise as its eyes turn back to brown.

QUEENIE *moves slowly forward, staring at the Occamy. As she does so she accidentally kicks a tiny glass bauble on the floor, which jingles as it rolls. At the sound, the Occamy rears up, screeching.* NEWT *tries to calm the large creature.*

NEWT
Woah! Woah!

JACOB *and* QUEENIE *stagger backwards to find cover. The Demiguise runs away and jumps into* JACOB'S *arms.*

The Occamy swoops, scooping NEWT *up onto its back as it violently thrashes about the attic, sending shelves flying.* NEWT *shouts out.*

NEWT
Right, we need an insect, any
kind of insect – and a teapot!
Find a teapot!

TINA *army-crawls through the chaos, dodging falling items, trying to find what* NEWT *has asked for.*

The wings of the Occamy crash down to the floor, narrowly missing JACOB *as he stumbles around, encumbered by the Demiguise now clinging to his back.*

NEWT *finds it harder and harder to hold on as the Occamy becomes more and more distressed, its wings now thrashing upwards, destroying the roof of the building.*

JACOB *turns, he and the Demiguise spotting a stray cockroach on a crate.* JACOB *reaches his hand up to grab it, when part of the Occamy crashes down, destroying the crate and his chance.*

ANGLE ON TINA, *crawling across the floor with great determination, in hot pursuit of a cockroach.*

ANGLE ON QUEENIE, *who screams as she's knocked to the floor by the force of the Occamy.* JACOB *runs up behind her and dives forwards, flat onto the floor, finally laying claim to a cockroach.* TINA *stands, clutching a teapot and screaming.*

> TINA
>
> Teapot!

At this noise, the Occamy rears its head once more, causing its tail to writhe, squashing and pinning JACOB – *with the Demiguise* – *against one of the rafters.*

JACOB *and* TINA *are now at opposite ends of the room, neither daring to move, swathes of Occamy scales between them.*

ANGLE ON JACOB *and the Demiguise* – *the Demiguise looks shiftily up to the side and promptly vanishes.* JACOB *slowly turns to follow the Demiguise's gaze* – *the Occamy's face is inches away from his own, staring with full intensity at the cockroach in his hand.* JACOB *barely dares to breathe.*

NEWT *peers round from behind the Occamy's head and whispers.*

> NEWT
>
> Roach in teapot . . .

JACOB *gulps, trying not to make eye contact with the huge creature next to him.*

> JACOB
> *(trying to soothe the*
> *Occamy)*
> Shhhh!

JACOB *widens his eyes at* TINA, *warning her of his intent.*

IN SLOW MOTION:

JACOB *throws the roach. We watch it soar through the air as the Occamy's body begins to move once more, uncurling and swirling round the room.*

NEWT *jumps from the Occamy's back, landing safely on the floor, while* QUEENIE *takes cover, placing a colander over her head.*

TINA *runs, teapot outstretched, hurdling over the Occamy's coils as she goes – a heroic sight. She lands on her knees in the centre of the room, the cockroach falling perfectly into the teapot.*

The Occamy rears up, shrinking rapidly as it rises, before diving down head first. TINA *lowers her head, bracing herself for a hit. The Occamy races down towards the teapot, and glides seamlessly inside.*

NEWT *races forwards and jams a lid on top of the teapot. He and* TINA *breathe heavily: relief.*

> NEWT
> Choranaptyxic. They also
> *shrink* to fit the available
> space.

ANGLE INSIDE the teapot – the now tiny Occamy gobbling down its cockroach.

> TINA
> Tell me the truth – was that
> everything that came out of
> the case?

> NEWT
> That's everything – and that's
> the truth.

SCENE 92
INT. NEWT'S CASE—SHORTLY AFTERWARDS—NIGHT

JACOB *holds the Demiguise's hand, leading it through its enclosure.*

> NEWT (O.S.)
> Here she comes.

JACOB *lifts the Demiguise up and into its nest.*

> JACOB
> *(to the Demiguise)*
> Happy to be home? Bet you're
> exhausted buddy. Come on –
> there you go – that's right.

TINA *is tentatively holding the baby Occamy. Supervised by* NEWT, *she places it gently into its nest.*

HOLD ON TINA *as she looks around at the Erumpent, now stamping through her enclosure.* TINA'S *face is full of wonder and admiration.* JACOB *chuckles at her expression.*

PICKETT *gives* NEWT *a sharp pinch from inside his pocket.*

> NEWT
> Ouch!

NEWT *fishes* PICKETT *out, holding him up on his hand as he walks through the various enclosures.*

We see the Niffler sitting in a small enclave, surrounded by its various treasures.

> NEWT
> Right . . . I think we need to
> talk. See, I wouldn't have let
> him keep you, Pickett. Pick,
> I would rather chop off my

hand than get rid of you ...
after everything you have
done for me – now come on.

NEWT *has reached* FRANK'S *area.*

> NEWT
> Pick – we've talked about
> sulking before, haven't we?
> Pickett – come on give me a
> smile. Pickett, give me a ...

PICKETT *sticks out his tiny tongue and blows a raspberry at*
NEWT.

> NEWT
> All right – now, that is
> beneath you.

NEWT *places* PICKETT *on his shoulder and starts busying*
himself with various buckets of feed.

ANGLE ON a photograph inside NEWT'S *shed, which*
shows a beautiful girl – the girl smiles suggestively.
QUEENIE *stares at the photo.*

> QUEENIE
> Hey, Newt. Who is she?

NEWT
Ah ... that's no one.

QUEENIE
(*reading his mind*)
Leta Lestrange? I've heard
of that family. Aren't they
kinda – you know?

NEWT
Please don't read my mind.

A beat as QUEENIE *drinks the whole story out of* NEWT'S
head. She looks both intrigued and saddened. NEWT *continues
to work, trying hard to pretend* QUEENIE *isn't reading his
mind.*

QUEENIE *steps forwards, closer to* NEWT.

NEWT
(*angry, embarrassed*)
Sorry, I asked you not to.

QUEENIE
I know, I'm sorry, I can't help
it. People are easiest to read
when they're hurting.

NEWT
I'm not hurting. Anyway, it
was a long time ago.

QUEENIE
That was a real close
friendship you had at school.

NEWT
(attempting to be
dismissive)
Yes, well, neither of us really
fitted in at school, so we—

QUEENIE
—became real close. For years.

In the background we see TINA, who has noticed that
NEWT and QUEENIE are talking.

QUEENIE
(concerned)
She was a taker. You need a giver.

TINA walks towards them.

TINA
What are you two talking about?

NEWT
Ah nothing.

QUEENIE
School.

NEWT
School.

JACOB
(*putting on his jacket*)
Did you say school? Is there
a school? A wizardry school
here? In America?

QUEENIE
Of course – Ilvermorny! It's
only the best wizard school in
the whole world!

NEWT
I think you'll find the best
wizarding school in the world
is Hogwarts!

QUEENIE
HOGWASH.

A gigantic crack of thunder. The Thunderbird, FRANK,
*rises into the air screeching, flapping his wings vigorously,
his body turning black and gold, his eyes flashing lightning.*

NEWT *stands, examining the bird, concerned.*

NEWT
Danger. He senses danger.

SCENE 93
EXT. SECOND SALEM CHURCH—NIGHT

GRAVES *Apparates in the shadows. Wand drawn, he slowly approaches the church, examining the scene of decimation. Rather than nervous, he seems intrigued, almost excited.*

SCENE 94
INT. SECOND SALEM CHURCH—NIGHT

The place is destroyed – moonlight filters through gaps in the roof, and CHASTITY *lies dead amid debris from the attack.*

GRAVES *slowly enters the church, wand still drawn. Eerie sobbing can be heard from somewhere in the building.*

MARY LOU'S *body lies on the floor in front of him – the marks on her face visible in the moonlight.* GRAVES *considers the corpse: a realisation dawning on his face – no horror, merely wariness and intense interest.*

FOCUS ON CREDENCE, *cowering at the back of the church, whimpering and clutching his pendant of the Deathly Hallows.* GRAVES *steps quickly towards him, bends down, cradling* CREDENCE'S *head. However, there's little tenderness to his voice as he speaks.*

> GRAVES
> The Obscurial – was here?
> Where did she go?

CREDENCE *looks up into* GRAVES'S *face – he is utterly traumatised and unable to explain – his face a plea for affection.*

> CREDENCE
> Help me. Help me.

> GRAVES
> Didn't you tell me you had
> another sister?

CREDENCE *begins to weep again.* GRAVES *places a hand on his neck, his face contorting with stress as he tries to remain calm.*

> CREDENCE
> Please help me.

> GRAVES
> Where's your other sister,
> Credence? The little one?
> Where did she go?

CREDENCE *trembles and mumbles.*

> CREDENCE
> Please help me.

Suddenly vicious, GRAVES *slaps* CREDENCE *hard across the face.*

CREDENCE, *stunned, stares at* GRAVES.

> GRAVES
> Your sister's in grave danger.
> We need to find her.

CREDENCE *is aghast, unable to comprehend that his hero has hit him.* GRAVES *grabs him and pulls him up onto his feet, as they Disapparate.*

SCENE 95
EXT. TENEMENT IN THE BRONX—NIGHT

A deserted street. GRAVES, *led by* CREDENCE, *approaches a tenement building.*

SCENE 96
INT. TENEMENT IN THE BRONX, HALLWAY—NIGHT

Inside, the building is miserable, dilapidated. CREDENCE *and* GRAVES *climb the stairwell.*

> GRAVES (*O.S.*)
> What is this place?

> CREDENCE
> Ma adopted Modesty out of
> here. From a family of twelve.
> She still misses her brothers
> and sisters. She still talks
> about them.

GRAVES, *wand in hand, looks around the landing – there are numerous darkened doorways stretching out in several directions.*

CREDENCE, *still shell-shocked, has stopped in the stairwell.*

> GRAVES
> Where is she?

CREDENCE *looks down – at a loss.*

> CREDENCE
> I don't know.

GRAVES *becomes increasingly impatient – he's so close to his goal. He marches forward into one of the rooms.*

> GRAVES
> (*contemptuous*)
> You're a Squib, Credence.
> I could smell it off you the
> minute I met you.

CREDENCE'S *face falls.*

> CREDENCE
> What?

GRAVES *marches back along the corridor to try another room. His pretence of care for* CREDENCE *all but forgotten.*

> GRAVES
> You have magical ancestry,
> but no power.

> CREDENCE
> But you said you could teach
> me—

> GRAVES
> You're unteachable. Your
> mother's dead. That's your
> reward.

GRAVES *points to another landing.*

> GRAVES
> I'm done with you.

CREDENCE *doesn't move. He stares after* GRAVES, *his breathing becoming shallow and quick, as though he's trying to contain something.*

GRAVES *moves through the dark rooms. A tiny movement somewhere close.*

> GRAVES
> Modesty?

GRAVES *advances cautiously into a derelict schoolroom at the end of a corridor.*

SCENE 97
INT. TENEMENT IN THE BRONX, DERELICT ROOM—NIGHT

ANGLE ON MODESTY *cowering in a corner, wide-eyed with fear and shaking as* GRAVES *approaches.*

> GRAVES
> (*whispering*)

Modesty.

GRAVES *bends down and puts his wand away – once
again playing the soothing parent.*

> GRAVES
> (*gentle*)
> There's no need to be afraid.
> I'm here with your brother,
> Credence.

MODESTY *whimpers with terror at the mention of*
CREDENCE.

> GRAVES
> Out you come now …

GRAVES *extends his hand.*

A faint jingle sounds.

*ANGLE ON the ceiling as cracks begin to appear,
spreading like a spider's web. Dust begins to fall as
the walls shake uncontrollably, the room beginning to
disintegrate around them.*

GRAVES *stands. He looks down at* MODESTY, *but she is
clearly terrified and not the source of this magic.* GRAVES

turns and slowly draws his wand, the wall in front of him collapsing as though turned to sand, revealing another wall ahead. MODESTY *is nothing to him now.*

As each wall collapses in front of him he is transfixed, elated, yet also aware that he has made a colossal error ...

The final wall collapses. He is facing CREDENCE, *who stares at him, unable to control his fury, his sense of betrayal, his bitterness.*

GRAVES
Credence ... I owe you an
apology ...

CREDENCE
I trusted you. I thought you
were my friend. That you
were different.

CREDENCE'S *face begins to contort, his rage tearing him from within.*

GRAVES
You can control it, Credence.

CREDENCE
*(whispers, making eye
contact finally)*
But I don't think I want to,
Mr Graves.

The Obscurus moves horribly beneath CREDENCE'S *skin. An awful inhuman growl comes out of his mouth, from which something dark begins to bloom.*

This force finally takes over CREDENCE, *his whole body exploding into a dark mass which hurtles forwards out of the window, narrowly missing* GRAVES.

GRAVES *stands, watching as the Obscurus zooms out and over the city.*

SCENE 98
EXT. TENEMENT IN THE BRONX—NIGHT

We follow the Obscurus as it churns and twists through the city, wreaking havoc: cars are sent flying, pavements explode and buildings are demolished – the Obscurus leaves only destruction in its wake.

SCENE 99
EXT. SQUIRE'S ROOFTOP—NIGHT

NEWT, TINA, JACOB *and* QUEENIE *stand on the rooftop underneath a large 'SQUIRE'S' sign. From the edge they have a clear view of the chaos going on below.*

> JACOB
> (*overstimulated*)
> Jeez ... is that the Obscuria-
> thing?

Sirens sound. NEWT *is staring, registering the scale of the destruction.*

> NEWT
> That's more powerful than
> any Obscurial I have ever
> heard of ...

A particularly loud explosion in the distance. The city beneath them is starting to burn. NEWT *thrusts his case into* TINA'S *hands and takes a journal from his pocket.*

> NEWT
> If I don't come back,
> look after my creatures.
> Everything that you need to
> know is in there.

He hands her the journal, barely able to make eye contact.

> TINA
>
> What?

> NEWT
> *(looking back to the*
> *Obscurus)*
> They're not killing it.

Their eyes meet – a moment full of what they might have said to each other – before NEWT *jumps from the roof and Disapparates.*

> TINA
> *(distraught)*
> NEWT!

TINA *slams the case into* QUEENIE'S *arms.*

> TINA
> You heard him – look after
> them!

TINA *also Disapparates.* QUEENIE *shoves the case at* JACOB.

> QUEENIE
> Keep holda that, honey.

She moves to Disapparate, but JACOB *hangs on to her and she falters.*

> JACOB
>
> No, no, no!

> QUEENIE
>
> I can't take you. Please let go
> of me, Jacob!

> JACOB
>
> Hey, hey! You're the one that
> said I was one of youse . . .
> right?

> QUEENIE
>
> It's too dangerous.

A further massive explosion in the distance. JACOB *tightens his grip on* QUEENIE. *She reads his mind and her expression changes to one of wonderment and tenderness as she sees what he went through in the war.* QUEENIE *is moved and appalled. Very slowly, she raises a hand and touches his cheek.*

SCENE 100
EXT. TIMES SQUARE—NIGHT

The scene is one of total chaos. Buildings are on fire, people scream and run in all directions, cars lie destroyed in the road.

GRAVES *prowls through the Square, oblivious to the distress around him, his focus concentrated on only one thing.*

The Obscurus writhes at one end of the Square, its energy angrier now – moving through layers of hurt and anguish, the products of isolation and torment – flecks of red light roaring from within. CREDENCE'S *face is just discernible*

within the mass, distorted, pained. GRAVES *stands before it, triumphant.*

NEWT *Apparates from further down the street and watches.*

>   GRAVES
>   *(shouting to reach*
>   CREDENCE *over the*
>   *almighty noise)*
> To survive so long, with this
> inside you Credence, is a
> miracle. You are a miracle.
> Come with me – think
> of what we could achieve
> together.

The Obscurus moves closer to GRAVES *– we hear a scream from within the mass as its Dark energy bursts out once more, knocking* GRAVES *to the ground. The force sends a shockwave round the Square –* NEWT *dives behind a fallen car for cover.*

TINA *Apparates into the Square and takes cover by another burning vehicle close to* NEWT. *They look at each other.*

>   TINA
> Newt!

> NEWT
> It's the Second Salem boy.
> He's the Obscurial.

> TINA
> *He's not a child.*

> NEWT
> I know – but I saw him – his
> power must be so strong –
> he's somehow managed to
> survive. It's incredible.

As the Obscurus screams once more, TINA *makes a decision.*

> TINA
> Newt! Save him.

TINA *dashes out towards* GRAVES. NEWT, *understanding, Disapparates.*

SCENE 101
EXT. TIMES SQUARE—NIGHT

GRAVES *is moving nearer and nearer to the Obscurus,*

which continues to scream and wail at his presence. He takes out his wand, poised . . .

TINA *runs into view behind* GRAVES. *She fires at him, but he turns just in time – his reactions marvellous, astounding.*

The Obscurus now vanishes. GRAVES, *thoroughly irritated, advances on* TINA, *deflecting her spells with perfect ease.*

> GRAVES
> Tina. You're always turning
> up where you are least
> wanted.

GRAVES *summons an abandoned car, which whooshes through the air, forcing* TINA *to dive out of the way, just in time.*

By the time TINA *has gathered herself up from the ground,* GRAVES *has Disapparated.*

<u>SCENE 102</u>
INT. MAJOR INVESTIGATION DEPARTMENT, MACUSA—NIGHT

A metallic map of New York City lights up to show areas of intense magical activity. MADAM PICQUERY, *surrounded by top Aurors, looks on, aghast.*

> MADAM PICQUERY
> Contain this, or we are
> exposed and it will mean war.

The Aurors immediately Disapparate.

<u>SCENE 103</u>
EXT. ROOFTOPS OF NEW YORK—NIGHT

NEWT *race–Apparates as fast as he can across the tops of buildings in pursuit of the Obscurus.*

> NEWT
> Credence! Credence! I can help you.

The Obscurus dives towards NEWT, *who Disapparates just in time, before continuing to chase it across the rooftops.*

As he runs, spells explode around him, disintegrating the rooftops. A dozen Aurors have appeared, attacking the Obscurus from ahead, and almost taking out NEWT, *who leaps for cover, trying desperately to keep up.*

The Obscurus veers to avoid the spells, leaving black snow-like particles that drift across the rooftops as it retreats screaming, and turns down another block.

In a particularly vigorous display, the Obscurus now rises dramatically up into the air, as spells in electric blue and white hit it from all angles. Finally it crashes to the ground and races along a wide, empty street – a black tsunami destroying anything in its path.

SCENE 104
EXT. OUTSIDE A SUBWAY STATION—NIGHT

A line of policemen stand with their guns aimed at the terrifying supernatural force powering towards them.

Their faces turn from confused alarm to total panic as they see the mass swarming ahead, making straight for them. They fire their guns – their efforts futile in the face of such a seemingly unstoppable kinetic mass. Finally

they disband, fleeing down the street, just as the Obscurus reaches them.

SCENE 105
EXT. ROOFTOPS/STREETS OF NEW YORK—NIGHT

ANGLE ON NEWT, *standing on top of a skyscraper looking out as the Obscurus rises up over the surrounding buildings and slams spectacularly into the ground just outside the City Hall subway entrance.*

Sudden quiet. A pulsing, heaving, screechy breathing emanates from the Obscurus where it rests at the entrance.

Finally, as NEWT *watches, we see the black mass shrink to nothing, and the small figure of* CREDENCE *descends the steps into the subway.*

SCENE 106
INT. SUBWAY—NIGHT

NEWT *Apparates into the City Hall subway, a long, mosaiced Art Deco station tunnel, which bears the signs of having been crossed by the Obscurus: the chandelier creaks, a few tiles have fallen. We can hear its deep breathing, cornered, like a frightened panther.*

NEWT *creeps along the platform, trying to find the epicentre of the sound, as the Obscurus slides down the ceiling.*

SCENE 107
EXT. SUBWAY ENTRANCE—NIGHT

Aurors surround the entrance to the subway. Pointing their wands at the pavement and into the sky, they draw an invisible energy field around the entrance.

We hear more Aurors arrive, among them GRAVES – *scanning, calculating and immediately taking charge.*

> GRAVES
> Bar the area. I don't want anyone
> else down there!

As the magical field is almost complete, a figure rolls underneath it and dashes unseen into the subway – TINA.

SCENE 108
INT. SUBWAY—NIGHT

NEWT *has reached the Obscurus in the shadows of a tunnel. Now much calmer, it gently swirls in the air above the train tracks.* NEWT *hides behind a pillar as he talks.*

> NEWT
> Credence ... it's Credence
> isn't it? I'm here to help you,
> Credence. I'm not here to
> hurt you.

In the distance we hear footsteps, the pacing controlled, deliberate.

NEWT *moves out from behind the pillar, and steps onto the train tracks. Within the mass of the Obscurus we can see a shadow of* CREDENCE, *curled up, scared.*

> NEWT
> I've met someone just like

you, Credence. A girl – a
young girl who'd been
imprisoned, she had been
locked away and she'd been
punished for her magic.

CREDENCE *is listening – he never dreamed there was
another. Slowly the Obscurus melts away, leaving only*
CREDENCE, *huddled on the train tracks – a frightened
child.*

NEWT *crouches on the floor.* CREDENCE *looks to him, the
tiniest trace of hope dawning in his expression: might there
be a way back?*

> NEWT
> Credence, can I come over to
> you? Can I come over?

NEWT *slowly moves forwards, but as he does so a sharp
burst of light blazes out from the darkness and a spell
strikes, throwing him backwards.*

GRAVES *marches down the tunnel with intense purpose.*

CREDENCE *begins to run as* GRAVES *fires further spells
at* NEWT, *who rolls out of the way towards the tunnel's
central pillars. From here* NEWT *tries to fire back, but his
efforts are easily deflected.*

CREDENCE *continues to lumber down the tracks but stops – a rabbit caught in the headlights – as a train approaches, its lights glaring from the darkness.*

It is up to GRAVES *to save* CREDENCE *– magically casting him out of the train's path.*

SCENE 109
EXT. SUBWAY ENTRANCE—NIGHT

MADAM PICQUERY *surveys the situation from under the magical forcefield.*

ANGLE FROM the crowd and police's POV:

People begin to swarm around the subway, their cries and chatter becoming louder as they stare at the magical bubble surrounding the subway. Reporters have appeared, photographing the scene with an increased frenzy.

SHAW SR *and* BARKER *push their way through the crowd.*

> SHAW SR
> That thing killed my son – I
> want justice!

CLOSE ON MADAM PICQUERY *as she looks out to the crowd.*

> SHAW SR (*O.S.*)
> I'll expose you for who you
> are and what you've done.

SCENE 110
INT. SUBWAY—NIGHT

GRAVES *stands on the platform, continuing to duel with* NEWT, *who stands on the train tracks.* CREDENCE *cowers behind* NEWT.

Finally, almost bored by NEWT'S *efforts,* GRAVES *casts a spell that ripples along the train tracks and down the tunnel, finally blasting into* NEWT, *throwing him high into the air.*

NEWT *lands on his back and* GRAVES *immediately sets upon him, casting spells in a whip-like motion with increasing vigour.* GRAVES'S *immense power is evident, as* NEWT *writhes on the ground, unable to stop him.*

SCENE 111
EXT. SUBWAY ENTRANCE—NIGHT

WIDE SHOT:

We see the luminous wall of vibrating energy now flashing with the power of the magic it contains.

LANGDON, *drunk, stares, enthralled and amazed by the spectacle.*

> SHAW SR
> *(to the photographers*
> *around him)*
> Look! Take photos!

SCENE 112
INT. SUBWAY—NIGHT

GRAVES *continues to whip* NEWT, *a manic, crazed look in his eyes.*

CLOSE ON CREDENCE, *further down the tunnel,
sobbing. He begins to shake, his face slowly turning black as
he tries to stop the kinetic mass from rising up within him.*

As NEWT *cries out in pain,* CREDENCE *succumbs to
the blackness – his body enveloped and overcome – the
Obscurus rising up and blasting down the tunnel towards*
GRAVES.

GRAVES *is mesmerised – he falls to his knees beneath the
vast black mass – pleading in wonder.*

GRAVES

Credence.

*The Obscurus lets out an unearthly scream and dives
towards* GRAVES, *who Disapparates just in time. The
Obscurus continues to blast around the tunnel.*

GRAVES *and* NEWT *Disapparate and Apparate around
the subway trying to avoid the Obscurus's path. This causes
the station to disintegrate even faster. Suddenly, the force
accelerates, becoming a giant wave that consumes the entire
space before flying out through the roof.*

SCENE 113
EXT. SUBWAY ENTRANCE—NIGHT

The Obscurus crashes up through the pavement, watched by wizards and No-Majs alike. It storms up a half-built skyscraper, windows shattering at every level, electric wiring exploding, until it reaches the skeletal framework of scaffolding above, which buckles perilously.

Below it, the crowd outside the magical cordon runs for cover, terrified.

The Obscurus forms a wide disc shape before plunging back down into the subway.

SCENE 114
INT. SUBWAY—NIGHT

The Obscurus screams and dives, bursting through the subway roof – for a split second, both NEWT *and* GRAVES *seem on the point of death as they lie on the tracks, cowering beneath this Dark force.*

TINA (O.S.)
CREDENCE, NO!

TINA *runs onto the tracks.*

Inches from GRAVES'S *face, the Obscurus freezes. Slowly, very slowly, it rises back up, swirling more gently, staring at* TINA, *who looks straight back into its weird eyes.*

> TINA
> Don't do this – please.

> NEWT
> Keep talking, Tina. Keep
> talking to him – he'll listen to
> you. He's listening.

Inside the Obscurus, CREDENCE *reaches out to* TINA, *the only person who has ever done him an uncomplicated kindness. He looks at her, desperate and afraid. He has dreamed of her ever since she saved him from a beating.*

> TINA
> I know what that woman did
> to you … I know that you've
> suffered … you need to stop
> this now … Newt and I will
> protect you …

GRAVES *is on his feet.*

TINA
(*pointing to* GRAVES)
This man – he is using you.

GRAVES
Don't listen to her, Credence.
I want you to be free. It's all
right.

TINA
(*to* CREDENCE, *calming
him*)
That's it ...

*The Obscurus is beginning to shrink. Its dreadful face is
becoming more human, more like* CREDENCE'S *own.*

*Suddenly Aurors begin pouring down the steps of the
subway and into the tunnel. More Aurors advance from
behind* TINA, *their wands raised aggressively.*

TINA
Shhhh! Don't, you'll frighten
him.

*The Obscurus lets out a terrible moan and begins to swell
again. The station is crumbling.* NEWT *and* TINA *wheel
around, arms akimbo, both trying to protect* CREDENCE.

GRAVES *spins to face the Aurors, wand at the ready.*

> GRAVES
> Wands down! Anyone harms
> him – they'll answer to me—
> *(turning back to*
> CREDENCE*)*
> Credence!

> TINA
> Credence …

The Aurors begin pelting the Obscurus with spells.

> GRAVES
> NO!

We see CREDENCE *from within the black mass, his face contorted, screaming. The tirade of spells continues and* CREDENCE *howls in pain.*

SCENE 115
EXT. SUBWAY ENTRANCE—NIGHT

The magical force field surrounding the subway breaks down as people continue to flee the scene. Only SHAW SR *and* LANGDON *stand steadfast.*

SCENE 116
INT. SUBWAY—NIGHT

Aurors continue to aim spells at the Obscurus, their efforts unrelenting and brutal.

Under this pressure, the Obscurus finally seems to implode – a white ball of magical light taking over from the black mass.

The force of the change sends TINA, NEWT *and the Aurors stumbling backwards.*

All power subsides. Only small tatters of black matter are left – floating through the air like feathers.

NEWT *gets to his feet, his face racked with deep-felt grief.* TINA *remains on the floor, crying.*

GRAVES, *however, climbs up, back onto the platform, as close as possible to the remnants of the black mass.*

The Aurors advance towards GRAVES.

> GRAVES
> You fools. Do you realise
> what you've done?

GRAVES *seethes as the others watch him with interest.*
MADAM PICQUERY *emerges from behind the Aurors, her*
tone steely, questioning.

> MADAM PICQUERY
> The Obscurial was killed on
> my orders, Mr Graves.

> GRAVES
> Yes. And history will surely
> note that, Madam President.

GRAVES *moves towards her along the platform, his tone*
threatening.

> GRAVES
> What was done here tonight
> was not right!

> MADAM PICQUERY
> He was responsible for
> the death of a No-Maj. He
> risked the exposure of our
> community. He has broken
> one of our most sacred laws.

> GRAVES
> (*laughing bitterly*)
> A law that has us scuttling
> like rats in the gutter! A
> law that demands that we

conceal our true nature! A
law that directs those under
its dominion to cower in fear
lest we risk discovery! I ask
you Madam President—
> *(eyes flashing to*
> *all present)*

—I ask all of you. Who does
this law protect? Us?
> *(gesturing vaguely to the*
> *No-Majs above)*

Or them?
> *(smiling bitterly)*

I refuse to bow down any
longer.

GRAVES *walks away from the Aurors.*

MADAM PICQUERY
(to the Aurors flanking her)
Aurors, I'd like you to relieve
Mr Graves of his wand and
escort him back to—

As GRAVES *moves down the platform a wall of white light*
suddenly appears in front of him, blocking his path.

GRAVES *thinks for a moment – a sneer of derision and*
irritation crossing his face. He turns.

GRAVES *strides confidently back along the platform, firing spells at both groups of Aurors facing him. Spells fly back at him from all angles, but* GRAVES *parries them all. Several Aurors are sent flying –* GRAVES *appears to be winning . . .*

In a split-second NEWT *pulls the cocoon from his pocket and releases it at* GRAVES. *The Swooping Evil soars around him, shielding* NEWT *and the Aurors from* GRAVES'S *spells, and giving* NEWT *time to raise his wand.*

With a sense that he's been holding this one back, he slashes it through the air: out flies a crackling rope of supernatural light that wraps itself around GRAVES *like a whip.* GRAVES *tries to hold it off as it tightens but staggers, struggles and falls to his knees, dropping his wand.*

TINA

> *Accio.*

GRAVES'S *wand flies into* TINA'S *hand.* GRAVES *looks around at them, a deep hatred in his eyes.*

NEWT *and* TINA *slowly advance,* NEWT *raising his wand.*

NEWT

> *Revelio.*

GRAVES *transforms. He is no longer dark, but blond and blue-eyed. He is the man on the posters. A murmur spreads through the crowd: GRINDELWALD.*

MADAM PICQUERY *moves towards him.*

> GRINDELWALD
> (*with contempt*)
> Do you think *you* can hold
> me?

> MADAM PICQUERY
> We'll do our best, Mr
> Grindelwald.

GRINDELWALD *stares intently at* MADAM PICQUERY,
*his expression of disgust turning into a small, derisory
smile. He is forced to his feet by two Aurors, who move him
towards the entrance.*

As GRINDELWALD *reaches* NEWT, *he pauses – both
smiling and sneering.*

> GRINDELWALD
> Will we die, just a little?

He is led away up and out of the subway. NEWT *watches,
bemused.*

TIME CUT:

QUEENIE *and* JACOB *push their way through to the front
of the Aurors.* JACOB *holds* NEWT'S *case.*

QUEENIE *hugs* TINA. NEWT *stares at* JACOB.

> JACOB
> Hey ... I figured somebody
> oughta keep an eye on this
> thing.

He hands NEWT *his case.*

> NEWT
> *(humble, completely*
> *grateful)*
> Thank you.

MADAM PICQUERY *addresses the group as she stares through the broken roof of the subway station, into the world outside.*

> MADAM PICQUERY
> We owe you an apology, Mr
> Scamander. But the magical
> community is exposed! We
> cannot Obliviate an entire
> city.

A beat as this sinks in.

As NEWT *follows* MADAM PICQUERY'S *gaze, he sees a tendril of black matter, a small part of the Obscurus, floating down through the roof. Unnoticed by anyone else,*

*it eventually floats up and away, trying to reconnect with
its host.*

A pause. NEWT'S *attention snaps back to the problem at
hand.*

NEWT

Actually, I think we can.

TIME CUT:

NEWT *has placed his case wide open underneath the huge
hole in the subway roof.*

PUSH IN CLOSE ON NEWT'S *open case.*

Suddenly FRANK *bursts forth in a flurry of feathers and
gushes of wind – the crowd of Aurors backs away. The
creature is beautiful, mesmerising but scary as he flaps his
powerful wings and hovers above them.*

NEWT *moves forward – he examines* FRANK, *a look of
real tenderness and pride on his face.*

NEWT

I was intending to wait until
we got to Arizona, but it
seems like now you are our
only hope, Frank.

A look between them – an understanding. NEWT *reaches*

out his arm and FRANK *presses his beak lovingly into the embrace – they nuzzle each other affectionately.*

The assembled group watches in awe.

> NEWT
> I'll miss you, too.

NEWT *steps back, taking the flask of Swooping Evil venom from his pocket.*

> NEWT
> (*to* FRANK)
> You know what you've got to
> do.

NEWT *throws the vial high up into the air –* FRANK *lets out a sharp cry, catching it in his beak and immediately soaring out of the subway.*

SCENE 117
EXT. NEW YORK—SKY—DAWN

No-Majs and Aurors alike shriek and recoil as FRANK *bursts forth from the subway, gliding into the dawn-lit sky.*

We follow FRANK *as he rises higher and higher into the air. As his wings flap harder, faster, storm clouds congregate. Lightning flashes. We spiral upwards as* FRANK *twists and turns, leaving New York lying far below.*

CLOSE ON FRANK'S *beak, the vial clutched tightly and finally crushed. The powerful venom spreads through the thick rain, enchanting it, thickening it. The darkening sky flashes a brilliant blue and rain begins to fall.*

SCENE 118
EXT. SUBWAY ENTRANCE—DAWN

HIGH ANGLE pushing down towards the crowd as they look up to the sky. As the rain falls and hits them, people move on, docile – their bad memories washed away. Each person goes about their daily business as though nothing unusual has happened.

Aurors move through the streets, performing repairing charms to rebuild the city: buildings and cars are reconstructed and streets are returned to normal.

ANGLE ON LANGDON, *standing in the rain, his expression softening, growing blank as the water runs over his face.*

ANGLE ON *police looking at their guns, confused – why
do they have them drawn? They slowly gather themselves,
putting their weapons away.*

*Inside a small family home, a young mother looks on
fondly at her family. As she takes a sip of water, her
expression becomes blank.*

*Groups of Aurors continue to repair the streets, swiftly
reassembling broken tram tracks, all traces of destruction
finally disappearing. One Auror, passing a newsstand,
enchants the papers, removing* NEWT *and* TINA'S
*mugshots and replacing them with banal headlines about
the weather.*

MR BINGLEY, *the bank manager, stands in his bathroom
taking a shower. As the water trickles over him, he too is
Obliviated. We see* BINGLEY'S *wife, brushing her teeth,
her expression vacant, carefree.*

FRANK *continues to soar through the streets of New York,
churning up more and more rain as he goes, his feathers
shimmering a brilliant gold. Finally he glides into the
breaking New York dawn, a magnificent sight.*

SCENE 119
INT. SUBWAY PLATFORM—DAWN

As MADAM PICQUERY *looks on, the roof of the subway is swiftly repaired.*

NEWT *addresses the group.*

> NEWT
> They won't remember
> anything. That venom
> has incredibly powerful
> Obliviative properties.

> MADAM PICQUERY
> *(impressed)*
> We owe you a great debt, Mr
> Scamander. Now – get that
> case out of New York.

> NEWT
> Yes, Madam President.

MADAM PICQUERY *begins to walk away, her pack of Aurors moving with her. Suddenly she turns back.* QUEENIE, *having read her mind, stands protectively in front of* JACOB, *trying to hide him.*

> MADAM PICQUERY
> Is that No-Maj still here?

(*on seeing* JACOB)
Obliviate him. There can be
no exceptions.

MADAM PICQUERY *reads the anguish in their faces.*

MADAM PICQUERY
I'm sorry – but even one
witness ... you know the law.

A pause. She is uncomfortable at their distress.

MADAM PICQUERY
I'll let you say goodbye.

She leaves.

SCENE 120
EXT. SUBWAY—DAWN

JACOB *leads the others up the steps of the subway,*
QUEENIE *following close behind him.*

*Rain is still falling heavily, the streets now almost empty
but for a few hard-working Aurors.*

JACOB *has reached the top of the steps and stands, gazing into the rain.* QUEENIE *reaches out and grabs his coat, willing him not to move out into the street.* JACOB *turns to her.*

> JACOB
> Hey. Hey this is for the best.
> *(off their looks)*
> Yeah – I was – I was never
> even supposed to be here.

JACOB *fights back tears.* QUEENIE *gazes up at him, her beautiful face full of distress.* TINA *and* NEWT, *too, look incredibly sad.*

> JACOB
> I was never supposed to
> know any of this. Everybody
> knows Newt only kept me
> around because – hey –
> Newt, why did you keep me
> around?

NEWT *has to be explicit. It doesn't come easily.*

> NEWT
> Because I like you. Because
> you're my friend and I'll
> never forget how you helped
> me, Jacob.

A beat. JACOB *is overcome with emotion at* NEWT'S
answer.

> JACOB
>
> Oh!

QUEENIE *moves forwards up the stairs towards* JACOB –
they stand close.

> QUEENIE
> *(trying to cheer him up)*
> I'll come with you. We'll
> go somewhere – we'll go
> anywhere – see I ain't never
> gonna find anyone like—

> JACOB
> *(bravely)*
> There's loads like me.

> QUEENIE
> No … no … there's only one
> like you.

The pain is almost unbearable.

> JACOB
> *(a beat)*
> I gotta go.

JACOB *turns to face the rain, and wipes his eyes.*

> NEWT
> (*starting after him*)
> JACOB!

> JACOB
> (*trying to smile*)
> It's okay ... it's okay ... it's
> okay. It's just like waking up,
> right?

*The group smiles back at him, encouraging, trying to soothe
the situation.*

Looking at their faces as he moves, JACOB *walks
backwards into the rain. Turning his face to the
sky, arms out, he allows the water to wash over him
completely.*

QUEENIE *creates a magical umbrella with her wand and
steps out towards* JACOB. *She moves in closely, tenderly
stroking* JACOB'S *face before closing her eyes and bending
in to gently kiss him.*

Finally she pulls slowly away, her gaze not leaving
JACOB'S *face even for a second. Then, suddenly, she's gone,
leaving* JACOB *standing, arms out, longingly embracing no
one.*

CLOSE ON JACOB'S *face as he fully 'wakes up', blank-faced and confused by his location and the torrential downpour he's standing in. He finally moves off through the streets – a lonely figure.*

SCENE 121
EXT. JACOB'S CANNING FACTORY—A WEEK
LATER—EARLY EVENING

An exhausted JACOB, *surrounded by a crowd of similarly
overalled production-line workers, is leaving after a hard
day's shift. He carries a battered leather case.*

A man walks towards him – NEWT. *They collide and*
JACOB'S *case is knocked to the ground.*

NEWT
So sorry – sorry!

NEWT *has moved swiftly and purposefully onwards.*

JACOB
(no recognition)
Hey!

JACOB *bends to pick up his case and looks down, puzzled.*
His old case is suddenly very heavy. One of the catches
flicks open of its own accord. JACOB *smiles a little, and*
bends down to open the case.

Inside, the case is filled with solid silver Occamy eggshells, a
note attached. As JACOB *reads, we hear:*

NEWT *(V.O.)*
'Dear Mr Kowalski, You are
wasted in a canning factory.
Please take these Occamy
eggshells as collateral for
your bakery. A well-wisher.'

SCENE 122
EXT. NEW YORK HARBOUR—NEXT DAY

CLOSE ON NEWT'S *feet as he walks through the crowd.*

NEWT *is preparing to leave New York, overcoat on, Hufflepuff scarf around his neck, case tied up tightly with string.*

TINA *walks alongside him. They stop before the boarding gate.* TINA *looks anxious.*

NEWT
(*smiling*)
Well it's been ...

TINA
Hasn't it!

Pause. NEWT *looks up,* TINA'S *expression is expectant.*

TINA
Listen, Newt, I wanted to
thank you.

NEWT
What on earth for?

TINA
Well, you know, if you hadn't
said all those nice things to
Madam Picquery about me –
I wouldn't be back on the
investigative team now.

NEWT
Well – I can't think of
anyone that I'd rather have
investigating me.

Not precisely what he was aiming for, but too late now ...
NEWT *becomes slightly awkward,* TINA *shyly appreciative.*

TINA

Well try not to need
investigating for a bit.

NEWT

I will. Quiet life for me
from now on ... back to
the Ministry ... deliver my
manuscript ...

TINA

I'll look out for it. *Fantastic
Beasts and Where to Find Them.*

Weak smiles. A pause. TINA *plucks up courage.*

TINA

Does Leta Lestrange like to
read?

NEWT

Who?

TINA

The girl whose picture you
carry—

NEWT

I don't really know what
Leta likes these days because
people change.

> TINA
> Yes.

> NEWT
> (*a dawning realisation*)
> I've changed. I think. Maybe
> a little.

TINA *is delighted, but doesn't know how to express it.
Instead, she's trying not to cry. The ship's siren sounds –
most of the other passengers have now boarded.*

> NEWT
> I'll send you a copy of my
> book, if I may.

> TINA
> I'd like that.

NEWT *gazes at* TINA – *awkwardly affectionate. He gently
reaches forward and touches her hair. Lingering for a
moment, they stare into each other's eyes.*

A last look and NEWT *suddenly moves away, leaving* TINA
standing, raising a hand to touch where NEWT *stroked her
hair.*

But then he's back.

NEWT
I'm so sorry – how would you
feel if I gave you your copy in
person?

A radiant smile breaks across TINA'S *face.*

TINA
I'd like that – very much.

NEWT *can't help but grin back at her before turning and walking away.*

He pauses on the gangplank, perhaps unsure of how to act, but eventually moves on without looking back.

TINA *stands alone in the empty harbour. As she walks away, there's a playful skip to her step.*

SCENE 123
EXT. JACOB'S BAKERY, LOWER EAST SIDE—
THREE MONTHS LATER—DAY

WIDE SHOT of a bustling New York street – market stalls line the street, which heaves with busy people, horses and carriages.

ANGLE ON a small, inviting bakery. Crowds throng outside the pretty little shop, painted with the name 'KOWALSKI'. People peer with interest into the shop's windows, and happy customers leave, their arms laden with baked goods.

SCENE 124
INT. JACOB'S BAKERY, LOWER EAST SIDE—DAY

CLOSE ON the doorbell as it rings to signal the entrance of a new customer.

CLOSE ON the pastries and breads on the counter, all moulded into fanciful little shapes – we recognise the Demiguise, Niffler and Erumpent among them.

JACOB, serving, is very happy, his shop full to bursting with customers.

> FEMALE CUSTOMER
> *(examining the little*
> *pastries)*
> Where do you get your ideas
> from, Mr Kowalski?

> JACOB
> I don't know, I don't know –
> they just come!

He hands the lady her pastries.

> JACOB
> Here you go – don't forget
> this – enjoy.

JACOB *turns and calls over one of his bakery assistants,
handing him a pair of keys.*

> JACOB
> Hey, Henry – storage, all
> right? Thanks, pal.

The bell tinkles again.

JACOB *looks up and is thunderstruck all over again: it's*
QUEENIE. *They stare at each other –* QUEENIE *beams,
radiant.* JACOB, *quizzical and totally enchanted, touches
his neck – a flicker of memory. He smiles back.*

THE
END

ACKNOWLEDGEMENTS

Without the patience and wisdom of Steve Kloves and David Yates, there would be no Fantastic Beasts screenplay. They have my boundless gratitude for every note, every piece of encouragement, every improvement they suggested. Learning, in Steve's immortal words, to 'fit the woman to the dress' has been a fascinating, challenging, exasperating, exhilarating, infuriating and ultimately rewarding experience that I wouldn't have missed for the world. I couldn't have done it without them.

David Heyman has been with me from the very first step of Harry Potter's transition to the big screen, and Fantastic Beasts would have been immeasurably poorer without him. It's been a very long journey since that first queasy lunch in Soho, and he is currently bringing to Newt all the knowledge, dedication and expertise that he brought to Harry Potter.

There would be never have been a Fantastic Beasts franchise without Kevin Tsujihara. Even though I've been carrying the germ of the idea for Fantastic Beasts since 2001, when I wrote the initial book for charity, it took Kevin to make me commit to bringing Newt's story to the big screen. His support

has been invaluable and he deserves the lion's share
of the credit for making this happen.

Last, but never least, my family have been
enormously supportive of this project even though
it has meant me working through a year's worth
of vacations. I don't know where I'd be without
you, except that it would be a dark and lonely place
where I wouldn't feel like inventing anything. So, to
Neil, Jessica, David and Kenzie: thank you for being
completely wonderful, funny and loving, and for
still believing that I should pursue Fantastic Beasts,
however tricky and time-consuming they may
sometimes be.

GLOSSARY OF FILM TERMS

Back to scene: After focusing on one character or action within a scene, the camera returns to the larger scene.

Close on: The camera films a person or object from close range.

Ext.: Exterior; an outside location.

Flashcut: An extremely brief transition shot, sometimes as short as one frame.

High wide: The camera is placed above, 'looking down' on the subject or scene from a wide angle.

Hold on: The camera rests on a person or object.

Int.: Interior; an indoor location.

Jump cut: Cutting from one important moment to the next from the same angle. This transition is usually used to show a very brief time lapse.

Montage: A series of shots in a sequence condensing space, time and information, often with music accompanying it.

O.S.: *Off-screen*; action that takes place off-screen or dialogue that is spoken without the character being shown on screen.

Pan/whip pan: Camera movement involving the camera turning on a stationary axis moving slowly from one subject to another; whip pan is a very fast move from one subject to the other.

POV: *Point-of-view*; the camera films from a particular character's point of view.

***Sotto voce*:** Spoken at a whisper or under one's breath.

Time cut: Cutting to later in the same scene.

V.O.: *Voice-over*; dialogue spoken by a character not present in the scene on screen.

Wide shot: The camera shows the entire object or human figure, usually to place it in relation to its surroundings. It is often used to set the scene in a film.

CAST AND CREW

Warner Bros. Pictures Presents
a Heyday Films Production
a David Yates Film

FANTASTIC BEASTS AND WHERE TO FIND THEM

Directed by............................... David Yates

Written by...................................... J.K. Rowling

Produced by .... David Heyman p.g.a., J.K. Rowling p.g.a.,
Steve Kloves p.g.a., Lionel Wigram p.g.a.

Executive Producers.......... Tim Lewis, Neil Blair, Rick Senat

Director of Photography .... Philippe Rousselot, A.F.C./ASC

Production Designer ....Stuart Craig

Editor ....Mark Day

Costume Designer ....Colleen Atwood

Music .... James Newton Howard

STARRING

NEWT SCAMANDER..................... Eddie Redmayne

TINA GOLDSTEIN.................... Katherine Waterston

JACOB KOWALSKI ....Dan Fogler

QUEENIE GOLDSTEIN .... Alison Sudol

CREDENCE BAREBONE .... Ezra Miller

MARY LOU BAREBONE.................Samantha Morton

HENRY SHAW SR .... Jon Voight

SERAPHINA PICQUERY.....................Carmen Ejogo

and

PERCIVAL GRAVES...........................Colin Farrell

ABOUT THE AUTHOR

J.K. Rowling is the author of the bestselling Harry Potter series of seven books, published between 1997 and 2007, which have sold over 450 million copies worldwide, are distributed in more than 200 territories and translated into 79 languages, and have been turned into eight blockbuster films by Warner Bros. She has written three companion volumes to the series in aid of charity: *Quidditch Through the Ages* and *Fantastic Beasts and Where to Find Them* in aid of Comic Relief; and *The Tales of Beedle the Bard* in aid of her children's charity, Lumos. Her website and e-publisher Pottermore is the digital hub of the Wizarding World. She collaborated with writer Jack Thorne and director John Tiffany on the stage play *Harry Potter and the Cursed Child Parts One and Two*, which premiered in 2016 in London's West End. J.K. Rowling is also the author of a novel for adult readers, *The Casual Vacancy*, and, under the pseudonym Robert Galbraith, of three crime novels featuring private detective Cormoran Strike, which are to be adapted for BBC television. *Fantastic Beasts and Where to Find Them* is J.K. Rowling's first screenplay.

ABOUT THE BOOK DESIGN

This book was designed by MinaLima, an award-winning design studio founded by Miraphora Mina and Eduardo Lima, who were graphic designers on *Fantastic Beasts and Where to Find Them* and on the eight Harry Potter films.

The cover and illustrations in this book were based on creatures in the story and inspired by 1920s decorative style. They were drawn by hand and finished digitally in Adobe Illustrator.

The text was set in Crimson Text and the display type was set in Sheridan Gothic SG.